HARLEY STREET

By Reginald Pound

Biographies
ARNOLD BENNETT
(William Heinemann Foundation Award)
NORTHCLIFFE (with Geoffrey Harmsworth)
SELFRIDGE
THE ENGLISHMAN:
A Biography of Sir Alfred Munnings, PRA
EVANS OF THE BROKE:
A Biography of Admiral Lord Mountevans
GILLIES: SURGEON EXTRAORDINARY
SCOTT OF THE ANTARTIC

Histories
THE LOST GENERATION
THE STRAND MAGAZINE: 1891–1950

Reminiscences
THEIR MOODS AND MINE
POUND NOTES
RUNNING COMMENTARY
A MAYPOLE IN THE STRAND

HARLEY STREET

Reginald Pound

London
MICHAEL JOSEPH

First published in Great Britain by
MICHAEL JOSEPH LTD
26 *Bloomsbury Street*
*London, W.C.*1
1967

© 1967 by Reginald Pound

To you, Anthea

Printed in Great Britain by
Western Printing Services Ltd, Bristol

AUTHOR'S ACKNOWLEDGMENTS

With the gracious permission of Her Majesty the Queen, I am able to publish, in Chapter XI of this book, extracts from letters written by the late King George VI to his speech therapist, Lionel Logue, CVO, who incorporated them in his notes.

*

Mr Valentine Logue, FRCS, and Mr Laurie Logue, have kindly allowed me to consult the notes and other records kept by their father, Lionel Logue, and to quote from them. I have been fortunate also in being able to draw on the recollections of Mr John Gordon, editor-in-chief, *Sunday Express*, a close friend of Lionel Logue.

To Miss A. Madeline Walker, of Hoylake, I am indebted for the opportunity of studying and quoting from the private papers of the late Sir Herbert Barker, her brother-in-law, the noted manipulative surgeon. Miss Walker also kindly answered many questions of biographical interest relating to him and his career.

Mr Joseph Eaton, of Messrs Eaton & Co., solicitors, Bradford, made available to me a transcript of the proceedings in Barker v. Thomas (1911), and gave me access also to correspondence that included letters written by Dr F. W. Axham, a central figure in the long running battle with medical orthodoxy that ensued.

Dr C. B. Heald, CBE, has likewise been generous with information, documentary help, and guidance. For particulars of

Harley Street property conditions I have had the advantage of recourse to Mr S. N. Owen (Messrs Hearne, Manners & Hearne) whose knowledge of the district is unrivalled.

My appreciation is extended also to the following:

Mr Robert Mackworth-Young, MVO, The Librarian, Windsor Castle; The Registrar, General Medical Council; The Curator, Royal Institute of British Architects; Col. J. H. Busby; Dr W. Ritchie McCrae; Dr William Sargant; Dr Peter Kerley; Mr Macdonald Hastings; The Publisher, *The Practitioner*; Mr C. M. Kohan, OBE; Mr A. R. Peers; The Rev. Jim Wilson; The Rev. Lewis Maclachlan and The Guild of Health; Dr Christopher Woodard; Howard De Walden Estates Limited; The Librarian, Royal Society of Medicine; The Librarian, Royal College of Physicians; The Librarian, Royal College of Surgeons of England; City Librarian, City of Westminster; Lady Waldegrave; Lord Inman; The Fellowship for Freedom in Medicine; Photographic Library, Greater London Council; National Monuments Commission; Borough Librarian, Swindon; Mrs G. Horder; The Rev. H. L. Cane; Mr Vivian Barrow; Dr R. D. Swaine; Mr Hugh Miller; and Mrs Kenneth Walker.

The papers of the late Sir Herbert Barker have been accepted by the Royal College of Surgeons of England for inclusion in its Library collections. That generous gesture will be specially appreciated by readers of this book who follow the course of the historic medical controversy narrated in it.

R.P.

CONTENTS

ILLUSTRATIONS

ACKNOWLEDGMENTS

Thanks are due to the following for permission to reproduce photographs in which they hold copyright: *Radio Times Hulton Picture Library*, 1, 2, 3, 11, 19; *The Press Association*, 4, 22; *Raymond Mander and Joe Mitchenson Theatre Collection*, 5; *Sir John Murray, K.C.V.O., D.S.O.*, 9; *New Health Society*, 10; *Lady Gillies*, 12; *Greater London Council*, 13, 15, 18, 21, 24, 25; *Syndication International*, 17; *Associated Newspapers Ltd*, 23; *Dinah Wathen Thompson*, 26, 28; *Topix*, 27.

THOSE EMINENT VICTORIAN DOCTORS

Two years before he was summoned to Berlin for consultation with German doctors about the ominous throat condition of Queen Victoria's son-in-law, the Crown Prince Frederick of Germany, Sir Morell Mackenzie, MD, of 19 Harley Street, regretted that the medical profession of England 'includes in its ranks no high functionaries of the realm. The truth is', he wrote, 'that we are just a little doubtful as to our position in the social scale.'[1]

Doubt was discounted in the popular mind by Harley Street's association with the Court through the long Victorian years, an era in which the ailments and, more particularly, the sufferings of royalty were a subject of absorbing public interest. Familiar from childhood, all too familiar, with the morbid elements in the religion of their fathers, the people were seemingly bemused by the realisation that those whom God had set in authority over them were granted no immunity from the changes and chances of this mortal life.

They heard with respectful relish the news that Queen Victoria's shriek at the death of the Prince Consort had echoed through the royal apartments at Windsor Castle on the morning of 14 December 1861. Eleven years later, in 1873, another royal death shriek sent a pleasurable shudder through the nation. Napoleon the Third, a patient of Sir Henry Thompson, FRCS, of 35 Wimpole Street, died at Camden Place, Chislehurst. His widow 'lifted up her arms, uttered a piercing cry, fell on the bed and gave her last kiss, then fainting away

[1] *Fortnightly Review*, 1885.

was carried to her room'.[1] From then on, the Empress Eugenie was an even more honoured guest in England.

The lingering fate of the German Crown Prince stirred the people's interest to a high pitch in 1887–8 by reason of his close connection with the royal house of England, and because a British surgeon was conspicuous in the case. A story went round in widening circles that the Crown Prince had been seen leaving Sir Morell Mackenzie's consulting room with the look of doom on his face.

Moving to Cavendish Square, Mackenzie soon had what his medical colleagues envied as the largest and most lucrative practice in the profession. The case of the German Crown Prince elevated him to extraordinary prominence. Known to every reader of the newspapers, he became a public figure in a way that no medical man has been since. Lady Duff Gordon recalled seeing 'people standing on chairs in a hotel restaurant to watch Mackenzie at dinner'.

While those sombre links with royalty established Harley Street in the common mind as the fount of recondite wisdom in matters of life and death, its reputation was tarnished by the controversy in which Mackenzie was involved as a sequel to his attendance on the Crown Prince. He had been invited to Berlin by the Crown Prince's German doctors. They were credited with having taken that initiative. No doubt in doing so they anticipated the approval of the Crown Princess, who was Queen Victoria's eldest daughter.

Jealousies, mutual distrust, clashing opinions, and the German official account of the illness of the Crown Prince, who decame emperor nine weeks before his death from cancer of the larynx in June 1888, provoked Mackenzie to publish a book on the case that affronted medical sensibilities in both countries. Over 100,000 copies were sold in the fortnight after publication. Mackenzie's Celtic temperament equated critics with enemies, and he was unsparing in his comments on the German surgeons who disagreed with his prognosis. That he had hesitated, rather than prevaricated, in giving a firm

[1] *Versatile Victorian*, by Sir Zachary Cope, MD (1951).

opinion appears to have been due to his suspicion that a syphilitic factor was involved. The possibility was presumably not
one to be comfortably discussed in royal circles either in
Germany or England. It was later confirmed by Mackenzie in
a private communication from him to a colleague. The case,
and its aftermath of recrimination, remains one of the most
embarrassing in medical annals. It also had political reverbera-
tions, for it generated animosities that entered into the growing
tensions between the two countries.

For Mackenzie, then fifty, it meant a partial eclipse that
lasted through the four years that were left to him. He had
incurred the powerful displeasure of the new ruler of Germany, the Kaiser of the First World War. At home, there were
libel actions against the German-born proprietor of the
St James's Gazette, and against *The Times*. He won them both,
and was given damages. He resigned from the Royal College of
Physicians, and was reproached by the British Medical Association and the council of the Royal College of Surgeons. He
lost much of his former prestige, though faithful patients continued to keep him still busy in his flower-filled consulting-
room, where his short-legged, high-backed 'operating chair'
was an object of fascinated interest because of its royal
associations.

Sir Morell was advising his women patients to discard their
feather boas and Medici collars, and telling the men who came
to him with throat complaints to throw away their mufflers
and to wear turn-down collars, a style made familiar to the
public by most of the great preachers of the day. Both sexes
were enjoined to gargle daily with cold salt water, as part of his
programme of throat hygiene. Through *The Strand Magazine*,
in 1892, he uttered what was probably the first public warning
of the risk of cancer from cigarette smoking.

Possibly with psychosomatic implications, his old affliction
of asthma returned during those last years to plague him with
what seemed like new virulence. He found relief only in the
continual smoking of stramomium cigarettes. His commendation of that means of relief was made to serve the purposes of a

crude advertising campaign that kept his name before the public for many years after his death.

The story was told over Harley Street dinner tables of his retort to Whistler, the artist, who impertinently consulted him about the health of his French poodle. Mackenzie sent a message to Whistler, asking him to make it convenient to call the the next time he chanced to be in Cavendish Square. The artist did so. 'Ah, Mr Whistler,' Mackenzie said, when his caller was announced, 'I am so glad to see you. I want your advice about painting my front door.'

*

Public confidence in the medical enclave known as Harley Street was restored when it became known that the Prince of Wales (later Edward VII) was a guest at one of the 'octave' dinners given by Sir Henry Thompson, Bart., FRCS, at 35 Wimpole Street. Those notable occasions, arranged for eight men of outstanding attainments or exceptional social distinction, beginning at eight o'clock, with eight courses on the menu, were a valuable liaison service to Harley Street through thirty years. Sir Arthur Conan Doyle was pleased to record in his autobiography that, on his being presented to George V shortly after the First World War, the King 'at once said: "Why, I have not seen you since that pleasant dinner when you sat next to me at Sir Henry Thompson's",' twenty years before.

It was part of the ritual of those evenings that the host should preface them with a dissertation on the food and drink that he had provided: the river from which the salmon was taken, the hills on which the saddle of mutton had been grown, the year and *cuvée* of the champagne, the history of the port and brandy. Anthony Hope, author of *The Prisoner of Zenda*, noted that Thompson himself 'ate next to nothing and drank water'.

He was the archetype Victorian medical man, one of the personages of an age that believed in individual greatness, especially of the kind that preserved its distance from the gaping multitude. His father was a Framlingham tradesman who at first objected to his son studying medicine on the ground that it would tend to encourage religious scepticism. He relented when his son, a migraine sufferer, suggested that medical training might help him to find the cause and cure of that distressing ailment. Young Henry Thompson advanced to the heights of the profession by specialising in quite another subject, urology. It is a branch of medicine requiring perhaps excessive tact. Thompson was wonderfully deft with the catheter and lithotrite. When a patient questioned his diagnosis by remarking: 'A rising surgeon tells me there is nothing wrong', Thompson snapped back at him: '*I* have risen.'

Summoned to examine King Leopold of the Belgians, he found the patient suffering from stone in the bladder, and obliged to sleep standing between two upright horsehair mattresses supporting his weight under the armpits. 'Within these, he stood face to the wall, his forehead resting on a soft folded napkin.' Only in that grotesque posture was he free of pain. Before the consultation, Thompson was deeply apprehensive. 'I slept only 1½ hours,' he told his wife in a letter, having 'got horribly anxious about the case in the night. No one knows how anxious but those who are placed in like circumstances.'

Using a plain-bladed lithotrite, he crushed a free stone in the King's bladder. 'My blades were full, I screwed home tight and withdrew them filled with a good quantity of phosphatic debris.' During a quarter of an hour's respite, surgeon and patient 'chatted about the American rifled guns', with what relevance can only be surmised. The bladder probing was then resumed. 'A slight trace of blood this time. Pain not much.' The operation was completed four days later.

The effect on the King's health and spirits was 'spoken of as miraculous'. Thompson's success gained him what he described in another letter to his wife as 'an ovation', a rare enough experience for a surgeon. He was in attendance on the King for five weeks, and was paid £5,000 for his services.

Two years after, the King sent for him again for what is now called 'a routine check'. The fee was £1,000.

Looking back on his successful treatment of the Belgian monarch, Sir Henry realised how much his insistence on using brand-new instruments contributed to it. He had observed that operations done by Civiale, the leading French urologist, with whom he was in close correspondence, were 'always followed by fever, while mine never were'. The explanation, he guessed, was in his having *employed instruments never before used*' (italics his). 'Hence unwittingly these new instruments were absolutely free from any trace of bacterial taint through previous use for other patients.' It was the practice to wash instruments, 'but mere washing is wholly inadequate to prevent the transmission of bacterial infection. It was to this happy accident that my success is greatly attributable.' The chief surgeon of the Middlesex Hospital, London, Sir John Bland-Sutton, looking back over those last Victorian years, said that 'the most dangerous items in a surgical operation were the instruments and the surgeon's fingers'.

Sir Zachary Cope, MD, has recorded that it was Sir Henry Thompson's custom to start his operating days at an early hour, so that he might follow up the cases quickly, and be less liable to night calls. The editor of *The World*, Edmund Yates, an 'octave' guest, made a note of 'the business-like accuracy' with which Thompson recorded his cases, 'in huge volumes kept under lock and key'.

Both Dickens and Thackeray were his patients; and there seems to have been significance in the omission of any reference to Dickens in Thompson's unpublished reminiscences, whereas Thackeray clearly engaged his sympathies. At their first consultation, he asked Thackeray how much wine he drank. 'Certainly several hundred bottles a year,' the novelist told him, adding extenuatingly: 'It's almost always other people's wine.'

Thompson was called to Thackeray's house in Palace Gardens, Kensington, on Christmas morning, 1863. The novelist had died in his sleep. 'Taken to his bedroom, I saw my friend', Thompson wrote, 'lying in a tranquil position

on his back with a placid countenance; both arms were outside
the bedclothes, the right curved round a hand-basin containing a little fluid which had evidently been vomited.'

Reporting the autopsy: 'The brain was examined, no haemorrhage had occurred but we were satisfied that death had
resulted from an attack of "serous apoplexy", with renal
degeneration. The weight of the brain was 58½ ounces; his
height was 6 ft. 3 in.; still in proportion to the height and
weight it was a large brain. Next morning the news made an
impression throughout the country as that of a sudden and
terrible calamity.' Thackeray was fifty-two.

On 6 August 1867, Dickens wrote: 'On sofa all night in
tortures,' a reference to the portentous pain in his left foot.
Thompson diagnosed gout. Dickens had an 'inward conviction' that it was not gout. He sought another opinion, which
may have accounted for Thompson's disregard of him in the
autobiographical notes.

Receiving the accolade of knighthood in 1867 at Osborne,
and meeting Queen Victoria for the first time, Thompson was
'impressed by the sweetness and charm of her clear low voice'.
Socially and professionally, his success was notable. The
Court being an abstemious one, his peculiar knowledge of the
urinary tract was presumably not of compelling interest. He
was invited as a guest, 'not as a doctor', to Balmoral by the
Queen, who, while retaining her regard for 'good kind Dr
Reid',[1] her resident physician, retained her custom of
announcing after dinner: 'I will receive the gentlemen and
Dr Reid in the drawing-room later.' Sir Henry Thompson
was shown favour also by the Empress Eugenie, whose 'beauty
and grace, associated with dignified and yet agreeable, almost
friendly manners', he never forgot. Her long afflicted husband
became his patient in 1872.

The Emperor told Sir Henry how greatly he had suffered
from his constitutional malady—'urinary trouble'—during the
battle of Sedan, 'being actively engaged on horseback for
several hours and during four or five of these in the very thick

[1] Later Sir James Reid.

of it, himself under fire'. Making his case notes, Thompson was 'inclined to infer' that as an alternative to his personal sufferings and to the possibility of defeat, Napoleon the Third 'rather courted than feared the closing of his career on the field of battle'. Sir Henry was a more sympathetic interpreter of the Emperor's moods than Bismarck, who remarked that Napoleon the Third was 'such a liar that you could not even believe the opposite of what he said'.

Sir Henry spent several weeks at the Court in exile at Chislehurst, finding 'the meals and social intercourse very pleasant and interesting'. At dinner, he was put on the Empress's left. Less inhibited than Queen Victoria, Eugenie spurred Thompson into talking across the table about his technique in diagnosing stone in the bladder. How could he, she asked, determine the form and size of an object inside the body when there was no possibility of seeing it? He answered, adroitly enough:

'Madame, I have beneath my feet at this moment a footstool which I have never seen, but I turn it over with my feet and find it has four legs of wood and a soft top, and that it is square. Now when I desire to determine the size and shape of a stone, I introduce a long silver instrument held in my hand and by lightly touching the stone I can judge more or less accurately of its size and form.' When he mentioned his belief that the stone that had so long troubled the Emperor was 'about the size of a date', the Empress ordered the manservant behind her chair, 'as only a vivacious woman of the Latin race would do' (Thompson), to bring in some dates for dessert, 'and the Doctor shall show me one of the size he means'. The specimen he held up for those at the table to see 'was examined with great curiosity and several expressions of shock at its magnitude'.

For his attendance on the Emperor, Sir Henry received a fee of £2,000. With the assistance of Mr Clover, 'the most experienced chloroformist of the day',[1] part of the bladder

---

[1] J. T. Clover (1825–82), a surgeon who pioneered developments in anaesthesia in the 1850s.

obstruction was removed, but long-standing kidney disease had undermined the patient's constitution. 'A sudden change occurred.' Sir Henry stood with his finger on the fading pulse, while a priest tried, and failed, to rouse the patient's understanding. 'Death without pain took place at 10.45.'

*

One of the first 'bedside baronets', Sir Henry Thompson was a man of distinguished appearance, to which it pleased Millais to do justice in a portrait. His deep-set eyes under their bushy brows gave him the look of a sage. His face, with its bold vane-like nose, was set off by one of the sumptuous Victorian moustaches that looked as if they were cultivated by a grower of incurved chrysanthemums. The eyebrows, the moustache, the lush silk cravat, and sweeping silk morning coat lapels, were a provocation to the cartoonists of *Vanity Fair*. His magisterial integrity protected him from the worst that they could do.

The dimensions of his personality were so much wider than those of ordinary medical specialists. He was a passable amateur painter in oils who exhibited at the Royal Academy. Under a pseudonym, he wrote novels of medical life, one of them a best-seller. Keen on astronomy, he built himself an observatory at East Molesey. He experimented with poultry farming, intent on improving certain breeds of bird. His study of dietetics, on which he wrote authoritatively, was only in part professional; he was an accomplished amateur chef, and a connoisseur of wine. Like many of the Victorians, he seemed to have the power to subdue time to his needs and purposes.

A leading advocate of cremation, who considered burial a social sin, he was the chief promoter of the Cremation Society of England, and its first president. Probably impelled by the earlier and horrific researches into the disposal of the dead by Dr George Walker and the reformer Edwin Chadwick, he originally projected the idea in an article in the *Contemporary Review* as long ago as 1874. A letter of his in *The Times* in

January 1904 brought about improvements in local authorities' handling of domestic refuse.

He never mastered his personal health problem, though experiment enabled him to alleviate it. Headache, vomiting, blurred vision, accompanied him down the years. Having satisfied himself that the attacks were linked with his consumption of beer and sweets, he finally decided that the real enemy was fermented liquor. Even when used in moderation, he concluded that, taken regularly, it did unrealised damage to the human organism. Deeming it a public duty to set forth his findings, he stated them in an open letter to the Archbishop of Canterbury. His appearance in that arena of controversy was greeted by opprobrious epithets. Fanatic was never one of them. His personal style was too measured for that.

His income averaged £8,000 a year, earned in nine months' work. He was a believer in the recuperative worth of a change of scene, and always spent his holidays abroad. His earliest travelling memories were of stage coaches. In the last two years of his life he became a motorist, and his handbook on *The Motorcar, Its Nature and Management*, is an interesting technical period piece. By then over eighty, he owned a 6½ h.p. car in which he made long runs in the south of England. Not merely content to enjoy the new experience, he 'took pains to examine every portion of the internal economy' of the little hooded Daimler 'York' Phaeton that stood outside his house in Wimpole Street, 'and to learn how its rapid and powerful movements were produced'.

Such zest for new knowledge is rare at that time of life. Sir Henry Thompson's was one of the inexhaustible temperaments of the age. He was out motoring, that eminent Victorian, three days before he died gently in his sleep in the spring of 1904. *The Times*, which had offended him by the brevity of its report of his summons to the bedside of the King of the Belgians forty years before, made handsome amends by giving him a monumental obituary notice, three and a half columns.

II

WHEN SPECIALISTS WERE SCORNED

Through Sir Henry Thompson; Sir James Paget (1814–99), who had two diseases named after him; Sir William Gull (1816–90), who said: 'They will come to me,' as he pulled a handful of guineas from his pocket—'they *will* come!' and Lord Lister (1827–1912), who operated on Queen Victoria for axillary abscess at Balmoral, receiving Her Majesty's approbation: 'A most disagreeable duty most pleasantly performed,' Harley Street formed a relationship with the Throne that made it part of what we now call the Establishment. What is rarely understood is that the specialists who sustained and amplified Harley Street's prestige had a harder fight to secure recognition within the profession than outside it; a neglected phase of medical history.

The faculty in general was not disposed to tolerate the creation in its midst of a class of experts who might acquire a status akin to that of barristers in the legal world. Specialists were not favourably regarded, either, by the medical colleges; and they were excluded from hospital appointments.

The 'popular prejudice for specialists' was the subject of the oration delivered to the Harveian Society by Sir William Gull in 1861. 'Who can treat as a specialty the derangements and diseases of the stomach, whilst its relations and sympathies are so universal?' he asked. 'How can there be a special "brain doctor", whilst the functions of the brain are so dependent upon parts the most distant, and influences the most various?' A tumour of the brain, he argued, might announce its presence through some disturbance elsewhere.

The orator was transmitting the spirit of his old teacher at

Guy's Hospital, Thomas Addison (1793–1860), whose name, like Paget's, was given to a disease, and who maintained that the true physician must have a good understanding of surgery, and the good surgeon a firm grasp of the principles of medicine. Addison 'dreaded becoming a specialist; it savoured of quackery'.[1] In the opinion of an anonymous contributor to the discussion, specialisation was 'the canker of medicine'. As late as 1903, Robert Brudenell Carter, FRCS, consulting ophthalmic surgeon to St George's Hospital, London, was advising readers of his book, *Doctors and Their Work*, to avoid specialists (in inverted commas) and 'to seek, rather, the advice of a physician or a surgeon who regards his calling as one and indivisible, and who recognises that the whole is greater than any of its parts'.

The first specialists were ophthalmic surgeons. Later in the nineteenth century, and not less derided, came the laryngologists. In 1876, Sir Morell Mackenzie told Dr Felix Semon, a German-Jewish ear, nose, and throat specialist newly arrived in Chandos Street, Cavendish Square: 'British medicine is extremely conservative and hates specialism. At present it is our specialty that has to bear the brunt of this antipathy, because it is the youngest.' Mackenzie developed the topic in an article for the *Fortnightly Review*:[2] 'At the dinner table, at the medical societies, in the gossip that relieves the aridity of scientific discussion, at all places where doctors most do congregate, specialism and its professors were denounced with a wealth of epithet that the controversialists of Billingsgate might have envied.'

Yet their advent was a logical consequence of the acceleration of medical research and discovery. New instruments, the ophthalmoscope in 1851, the laryngoscope in 1855, advances in anaesthesia and bacteriology, were an incentive to exclusive study and practice. Queen Victoria had not long been dead when the first radiologists put up their plates in Harley Street.

Remarking that 'by many specialism is held to be the crowning mercy of medicine', while others thought it 'an overgrowth

[1] *Eminent Doctors* (1885).   [2] June 1885.

needing repression', *The Lancet* later insisted that the modern specialist was a creation of the public and not of the profession. 'The public is obsessed by the glamour of specialisation', a situation largely brought about by a more widely informative press obsessed by 'names'. *The Lancet* looked forward to 'a regenerated medical profession' in which specialised practice 'would grow through the channels of the general practitioner and not by public demand'.[1]

Thirty-five years after, *The Practitioner* deplored 'the apparent complacency with which those in authority are accepting the disintegration of the profession into increasingly independent and vocal sects of specialist'. Dr F. T. Fox had dealt with the subject in his recent address to the Medico-Legal Society. 'There are only three sorts of lawyers,' he said, 'judges, barristers and solicitors. But in medicine we have about twenty-five "ologies", several kinds of "icians", some "ists" and numerous "itioners".' *The Practitioner* suggested that 'the time had come to call a halt to this schismatic process'. Stirring echoes of the protests of Addison and others long gone, it reminded the profession that 'the human being is not a conglomeration of integrated systems. He is an individual, with a personality of his own, and unless the individual is treated as such, the whole basis of our civilisation crumbles to dust.'[2]

Students of the growth of medical specialism would presumably ponder the inferences to be drawn from the individual practitioner's choice of subject in which to specialise. To what extent is it dictated by unconscious bias? There is often no doubt a reason more complex than that of the medical student who explained to Professor Sir Arthur Keith, at Edinburgh, that as a child he wanted to know how babies were born and, as no one would tell him, he decided to 'go in for medicine' as a means of finding out.

Plato considered it wisdom for a patient to choose a doctor who himself had suffered the illness he was being asked to treat. A specialist's preference for ophthalmology might

[1] 19 October 1918.   [2] *The Practitioner*, June 1953.

provoke interesting speculation. 'Focusing on the problems of others is a well-known form of resistance manifested by people undergoing psychoanalysis. Usually it is precisely the problem they do not wish to see in themselves.'[1] It would probably not be difficult to find psychiatrists who were neurotics.

Sir James Berry, FRCS, of 21 Wimpole Street, was an authority on hare-lips and cleft palates, of which congenital defects he was himself a victim. George Cathcart, FRCS, of 52 Harley Street, was afflicted in his youth by the double handicap of a lisp and a stammer. To overcome them, he studied voice production at Naples under a master of the old Italian *bel canto* school. He became one of London's leading throat specialists.

*

What took the specialists to a part of the town that Disraeli thought 'flat, spiritless, and dull', Dickens disliked, and Sir Walter Besant, the London historian, described as 'cut out of cardboard'? The question mark remains, probably because the answer lay in drift rather than in design. The first Harley Street fortune was made by an Irish quack named John St John Long, in the 1830s. That the queues at his door at No. 41 (now 84) were an incitement to reputable medical men to settle in the same street may be doubted. Not until the 1860s were more than a dozen or so doctors practising there, and for many years after private residents easily outnumbered them. Harley Street, then, had its own public-house, the *Turk's Head*, No.51.

Taking its name from the Harley family, whose chief ornament was Robert, Earl of Oxford, Queen Anne's Lord High Treasurer, Harley Street was originally part of a Cavendish estate venture at developing the land north of the now much mutilated square, dated from 1717, that continues to be identified with them in name. Edward Harley, Robert's son, had married Lady Henrietta Cavendish. The plan was to build 'residences for the nobility and gentry', who might be expected

[1] *The Wild Analyst*, by Carl Grossman (Barrie & Rockliff, 1965).

to keep up with the Cavendishes in tone if not in style. Allegedly as a consequence of the South Sea Bubble, it was only partly carried out. Leases of land were then granted to separate developers, who produced the present layout of parallel and hyphen streets, all bearing names tactfully commemorating the Cavendish marital ramifications: Devonshire, Portland, Welbeck, Chandos, Wigmore, Wimpole, Mansfield, Weymouth, Bentinck, Bulstrode, De Walden.

Some of the Harley Street houses were built by the able and long forgotten Leicester architect, John Johnson (1732–1814), county surveyor of Essex, whose office was in Berners Street. W. Thomas Collins, FSA (1735–1830), was responsible for extensions to the street in association with John White (d. 1813), surveyor to the Duke of Portland. The famous name of Wyatt is attached to the history of No. 10 (formerly No. 4), built in the early 1820s and bought for £6,000, apparently during its construction, by Captain the Hon. William Waldegrave, afterwards the eighth earl of that name. James Wyatt's son Benjamin supervised the completion and decoration of the house, one of the largest in the street. It had the rare novelty of a bathroom, 'with faucet and sluice'.

In general, Harley Street dates from the late eighteenth century, its various elevations marking the activity of its different builders. The west side, and that part extending from Queen Anne Street to No. 122, remain today in the possession of the Howard De Walden family, to whom it came by inheritance in 1854.

Disraeli's hint of mediocrity was belied by many of the interiors, in which pillared halls, carved mahogany doors, staircases with gracefully scrolled iron balustrades, embossed or painted ceilings, Adam mantelpieces, compensate for the stark classicism of the façades. The staircases and ceilings of Nos. 13, 22, 26, 71, 78, 81, are splendid survivals from the age of elegance. The fanlights and ceilings of 75, 77, 80, 86 and 96 likewise remind us that originally the doctors were a parvenu minority among the retired ambassadors, admirals and generals, and cousins of the nobility, who were long the principal residents. By the testimony of the Royal Academy catalogue for 1800, Turner, the artist, lived at 64 (now 51). In 1876, Gladstone took No. 73 as his London residence. Its windows were smashed by a mob incited to protest against his Eastern policy.

The strictly professional element did not obtrude until shortly after the middle of the century. By 1873, thirty-six medical men had addresses in Harley Street, presumably because of the proximity of well-to-do patients. Following the example of the more august private residents, including members of the Duke of Wellington's family, the doctors took care to add Cavendish Square to the address on their notepaper, a touch of Victorian *hauteur* that persisted until after the First World War.

It can reasonably be surmised, too, that the immanence of the great railway termini of Paddington, Euston, St Pancras, and King's Cross, had an effect on Harley Street's specialised future, there being then few established consultants in the provinces. It meant a readier availability of London experience and advice at the recognised fee for 'country journeys' of a guinea a mile up to two-thirds of the distance according to Bradshaw, 'the best paid part of the practice of the average London specialist', according to Sir Felix Semon (1849–1921) the laryngologist, who had moved to 59 Welbeck Street. The real change of status in Harley Street came with the telephone and the motorcar, enabling consultants to move more freely with the trends in residential fashion instead of being tied, as many formerly were, to hospital environments.

Sir Astley Cooper (1768–1841), who removed the sebaceous cyst from George IV's head, was asked why he did not give up his post at Guy's Hospital for West End practice. He answered: 'Here in the City people take off their hats to me. There I would have to take my hat off to them.' Savile Row was the fashionable medical address, with its easy access to the houses of the rich in Hanover Square and Piccadilly

Migrants to Harley Street, in later years, were advised to study the digits on the doors before settling down to practice.

'You'll be committing professional suicide,' Sir John Tweedie, FRCS was warned when in 1886 he moved five hundred yards north from No. 24 Harley Street to No. 100. The lower numbers are at the Cavendish Square end and were considered a guarantee of superior status. Sir Victor Horsley, the brain surgeon, told a newly qualified man: 'Mind you start in the right place. I started in Gower Street. That was a great mistake. Since I moved to Cavendish Square I've had nothing to complain of.'

*

That Dr George Harley (1829–96) should practise in Harley Street (No. 25) and bring up his family there seemed like the action of a natural law rather than an affectation of distinction. He was proud of his ancestry, rooted in Haddington, East Lothian, and liked to suggest, if not to state, that it was linked with the line of earls from which the street took its name. To be called 'Dr Harley of Harley Street' was for him a peculiar pleasure.

He was a medical scientist whose reputation was endorsed by the Royal Society, which made him a Fellow. His career examplified the questing spirit of the age in scholarship and science, the Victorian urge to subject all the problems of life to the scientific method. He had the typical curiosity, courageous in its application, tireless in its persistence, prolific in its impressions. He exposed himself to the dangers of auto-anaesthesia; risked being bitten by a mad dog in Paris; narrowly escaped execution as a spy in Trieste; stood in the front rank of the crowd watching the beheading of a criminal in Bavaria—'a gruesome spectacle! The first jets of blood must have risen at least three feet.'

As a medical student, he gained early professional notoriety by successfully delivering a seven-months child by Caesarian section, when no other help was available. He experimented on himself by living exclusively for several days on a diet of asparagus, his purpose being 'to stimulate diabetes'. In a similar excess of scientific curiosity, he swallowed several drops of pure nitro-glycerine and nearly brought his career to a close. His pulse rate shot up to 130 and as suddenly fell to 40, producing paralysis in the legs and feet.

Desiring, perhaps, to emulate the social success of Sir Henry Thompson and his 'octaves', Harley instituted his Sunday morning breakfasts for ten or twelve guests. They were occasions of gastronomic adventure, with Pomeranian goose breasts, donkey sausage or 'thousand-year-old' eggs from China, likely to be the *chef d'oeuvre*. The guests were usually medical men of repute, like Sir Richard Quain and Sir James Simpson; but Harley also enticed Dickens, Landseer, Leech, and Cruikshank to his table.

The Lancet for February 1868 told of the fate that struck Dr Harley when he was giving a course of lectures on medical jurisprudence at University College, London. After fifteen years of continuous work with the microscope, he noticed late one night that blood appeared to speck the lens. He cleaned the lens and put it back. Blood still showed. It was the onset of a long period of suffering from 'retinitis, followed by glaucoma in both eyes' (his own diagnosis). 'Light became unbearable; the employment of an ophthalmoscope by an oculist set up an acute attack of inflammation which nearly drove me mad.' As a scientist, he was not likely to dramatise his distress, and his account of it makes poignant reading. With the prospect of total darkness before him, he thought of suicide, 'remembering that an ancient philosopher had said that "the mere act of self-inflicted death is the strongest proof that a man can give of his sovereignty over himself".' His wife's devotion held him back, 'besides which, I had not lost hope'.

Incapable of sleep, and probably a more reliable witness to that deprivation than most insomniacs, he became a victim of the morphia habit. 'What a blessed change from the torments of the damned!' He cured himself of it by one of those acts of will that seem godlike to weaker natures. Proclaiming his intention to give up the drug, he was warned by a doctor friend: 'Don't boast. You too are human, like the rest of us.' Harley answered: 'Man, if I made up my mind to cut off my arm, I would do it. With the morphia bottle within reach, I shall lie here until nature gives me sleep again, or until I change my mind.' For the next eight nights he had no sleep—'not one wink'. Then the morphia spell was broken. 'I was rewarded by ten hours of sweet repose, and awoke comforted and refreshed.'

For many months he lived in two rooms at Shaldon, Devonshire, the windows covered with layer on layer of dark calico blinds extended across the walls to exclude the faintest chink of light. With bandaged eyes he sat at meals, and took exercise by walking round a circular table, timing himself by the striking of the clock. The sensitivity of his eyes was such that he shrank even from starlight.

He documented his heightened tactile awareness and the effect of his affliction on his visual imagination. 'A blind man lives in an ideal world surrounding him,' and he reported the results of an experiment he made to discount the popular notion that 'a blind person has just appreciation of the things with which he comes in contact.' He asked that his amanuensis should be described to him—'the colour of her hair, her complexion, figure, size, features, manners'. Another young woman who visited the house was likewise described to him, 'with the same minuteness'.

A few weeks before his liberation from darkness, 'I felt every feature of their faces with my hand. By repeating this operation at intervals of a few days, I imagined that I had formed a true picture of them both and that I should not experience the slightest difficulty in recognising the one from the other when I really saw them before me.'

The day came when the bandages were to be removed. Dr Harley sat in a subdued light facing the door of his study. 'Another couple of girls, comparative strangers to me, were also to enter, walk twice round the table, and then retire without uttering a syllable. One after the other, all four entered the room, went through the little pantomime indicated, and withdrew.' He underlined the result of the test. '*I failed to recognise* either of my fair friends! In fact, I expressed my strong conviction that a trick had been played upon me, for not one of the damsels realised in the slightest degree the picture I had formed either of my amanuensis or her companion. When they spoke I instantly recognised them; but, oh, what a disappointment!'

He hid his feelings, he wrote, for none of the girls matched his expectation. Ruefully, he concealed that he had been 'living under a delusion'. What struck him as 'the most curious thing of all' was that it was many weeks before he could dissociate his visual image from the reality. 'That is to say, when they were not actually before my eyes, and I spoke of or thought of them, it was the ideal, not the real, individual that presented itself before my mind's eye.'

Recovering at last, he noted that his sight was more acute, 'excessively so', his daughter thought; and for the time being he was without the power to discriminate between colours. All mauves, blues, greens and yellows appeared to be white, while greys, browns and reds looked black. He regained his colour sense by 'practising with bits of silk'. He had also lost the faculty of judging distance, from which he deduced that it is a product not of instinct but of education.

Returning to his 'ruined practice' in Harley Street, with only two patients on his books during the next few weeks, he continued to widen his interests with extraordinary verve. Spelling reform and champagne were two of the diverse subjects that took his attention. He abolished all double consonants from his correspondence (excepting only personal names) and from articles he wrote for medical and scientific journals, setting forth his views and proposals in a book, *The Simplification of English Spelling*.

'The number of double consonants which infest English literature is far beyond the power of human computation. A glance at *The Times* newspaper will suffice to illustrate the truthfulness of this assertion.' In concert with his oft-repeated assessment of the respective importance of fact and supposition (a cliché of his conversation), he produced the surprising information that 'each full-sized copy of the newspaper contains more than 30,000 doubled bs, cs, ds, fs, and gs, etc.—absolutely unnecessary letters of the alphabet, which not only take up valuable space, but must have consumed much time in writing and printing'. He suggested that the newspaper might save 'about £10,000 a year by their abolition'.

It was in his drawing-room at 25 Harley Street, *circa* 1887, that a new scientific instrument producing sounds recorded on a perforated wax plate was first heard in London, an early intimation of the gramophone. George and Weedon Grossmith, authors of *The Diary of a Nobody*, shared in the amazement of those present.

Three months before his death, Harley published in the *Contemporary Review*[1] his findings on the merits of champagne, causing 'a perfect furore among wine merchants', wrote his daughter, Mrs Alec Tweedie. The gist of his thesis was that 'sweet wines do not give gout, but "sec" or so-called "sec" wines do'. His analysis of the process by which the grape becomes champagne still makes fascinating reading.

Dr Harley exercised the scientific temper to the end, which came in 1896, when he was sixty-nine. In his cash-box he left a letter ordering an autopsy to be carried out 'for the benefit of others'. That done, his body was to be cremated, 'the ashes weighed, and the facts noted'. He forecast their weight with uncanny accuracy.

One of his closest friends, in a *post mortem* tribute, saw him as a disappointed man, reflecting that 'success and failure lie not in what a person has done, but in what he hoped to do'. That Dr George Harley hoped for more than his destiny provided we cannot know. His *Diseases of the Liver* was considered his *magnum opus*, a more imposing monument than his *Urine and its Derangements*, dictated, while he was blindfolded, to his 'lady amanuensis'.

*

By 1900, the medical population of Harley Street numbered 157, though it was as yet a rare thing for more than one name

[1] June 1896.

plate to be seen on a door. Ten years later the figure was 214. Harley Street had become a hallmark rather than an address, its prestige cast over Wimpole Street, Welbeck Street, Queen Anne Street, Weymouth Street, New Cavendish Street, Devonshire Place, and Portland Place, all having a satellite relationship with it and basking in its increasing fame. Surgeons and physicians practising in those streets were considered to be of Harley Street provenance. 'But that is not a doctors' street,' Sir Henry Thompson had been told in surprise when he took his first consulting-room in Wimpole Street. 'Very well,' he replied, 'I'll make it one.' Tennyson thought that Wimpole Street was 'long and unlovely', Virginia Woolf that it was 'the most august of London streets'.

Harley Street, which after no more than three years (1847–1850), rid itself of the embarrassment of its *Turk's Head* public house, continued to maintain St Peter's, Vere Street, often referred to as 'the doctors' church', an apanage of All Souls, Langham Place, to which St Peter's rendered its offertories, subject to the good nature of the incumbent of the parent living. Its pews were filled by doctors and their families. Prominent among them were Sir Thomas Watson, MD (1792–1882) and Sir Andrew Clark, MD (1826–94). Sir Thomas was the Nestor of the profession who through most of his ninety-three years drank milk every day and ate sparingly. Near the end of his life, he declared: 'When I was a young doctor, I was always keen to try new remedies. Now I find that the old ones are just as good.'

Sir Andrew Clark was Gladstone's doctor, a deeply religious man whose patients were reminded of it by the inscription on a wall of his consulting-room at 16 Cavendish Square: *Glory Be To God*. He had a possibly morbidly obsessive concern for the truth in all things, great and small. A young woman, walking with him in the garden at his country house at Essendon, observed that 'the caterpillars have eaten the gooseberry bushes'. She was reprovingly corrected: 'leaves—*not* bushes.'

To the end of his life, he rose at 6 a.m., six days a week, to

Sir Morell Mackenzie: 'We doctors are just a little doubtful as to our position in the social scale.' He is seen here (*front*, *right*) in consultation with German physicians and surgeons about the case of the Emperor Frederick.

Sir Victor Horsley, the founder of modern brain surgery.

Sir Frederick Treves. His success as a Court surgeon confirmed Harley Street's role as part of the Establishment.

Buckingham Palace, 1910. Londoners reading the bulletin announcing the death of Edward VII.

deal with his large professional correspondence, writing all his letters himself. He was making £12,000 a year in the 1880s. 'Considering the number of patients who can comfortably be seen between 9 and 2 o'clock,' he remarked to a colleague, 'and the number of visits I can manage between 2 and 7, I see no hope of improving on that figure.'

Harley Street men of the period were commonly seen hurrying from their doorways to the nearest pillar-box around midnight, 'catching the last post'. The scholar-physician, Sir Humphrey Rolleston (1862–1944) met a celebrated senior specialist posting a great quantity of letters at that hour. Rolleston, then a beginner in Harley Street, wondered aloud how the great man coped with so heavy a mail. He was told: 'When it gets really beyond me, I have a bottle of port.' Rolleston looked puzzled. It was then explained to him: 'My dear fellow, when I've had a bottle of port I don't give a damn whether I write my letters or not.'

A magazine symposium of the '90s, illustrated by photographs of doctors who were in the public eye, shows that the majority wore beards as if in solemn confirmation of the legend that Adam was created with hair on his face. Their immediate predecessors had been mostly clean shaven. Beard wearing in modern English society dates from the Crimean period. The campaigners by land and sea grew beards as chest protectors in extreme cold. Returning, they set a fashion. Its prophylactic value was commended to the Rev. A. J. Church, the Victorian author of *Memories of Men and Books*, as a safeguard 'against affections of the throat'. When he added a moustache, he was reprimanded and ordered to shave it off by the Court of Merchant Taylors' School, where he was an under master.

The invention of the stethoscope was welcomed as a refinement of more than auscultatory techniques. It gave confidence to the bearded physician listening to the heart sounds of female invalids, and also, according to Sir William Arbuthnot Lane's biographer, 'banished the risk of picking up their fauna from his poorer patients'.

*

Harley Street's high noon, the golden age of consulting practice, was the first decade of the new century, when white spats were the insignia of medical eminence where formerly it was the gold-knobbed cane with the concealed pomander of sweet-smelling herbs; when frock coats and silk hats were 'the livery of the laborious week'; when the fixed fee was two guineas for the first consultation, three guineas for visits within four miles of Charing Cross; when there was a manservant at every other door, the surgeon's carriage-and-pair and the physician's one-horse brougham had not been finally displaced by the motorcar; and Sir Frederick Treves, Bart., GCVO, FRCS (1853–1923), of 6 Wimpole Street, was the great exemplar of medical authority and distinction.

With his square shoulders and military moustache, Treves looked like a regimental bandmaster. As Serjeant Surgeon to Edward VII and later to George V, and Surgeon-in-Ordinary to Queen Alexandra, he carried himself as if he was on parade. His professional eminence was in strong contrast with the modesty of his early ambition. He had wanted to be a country doctor.

He did not state his parentage in *Who's Who*. He was the son of William Treves, upholsterer, of Dorchester, the first in a long line of farmers on both sides of the family to desert the land. In his childhood, he came under the tutelage of the Rev. William Barnes, the Dorset dialect poet, who walked the streets of the county town in Quaker garb, the long stockings, the vast brimmed hat. Afterwards, Treves went to Merchant Taylors' School, London. From there he entered the London Hospital as a medical student, marked out from the first by his precise habits of mind and expression and a gift for exact observation.

He qualified as a surgeon in 1876. After two years' general practice in Derbyshire, fulfilling an early dream, and having married, he retraced his steps to London, becoming successively surgical registrar and, at the age of thirty-two, chief surgeon at his old hospital. The then house governor of London Hospital recalled that Treves's operating coat was so stiff with congealed blood that it would 'stand upright when placed on the floor'. In the operating theatre he worked deftly and decisively, and often with remarkable courage. Ordinarily, he wore spectacles for his myopia. At the operating table, he took them off to peer closely at his incisions.

His anatomy lectures and demonstrations were crowded occasions, and he wrote textbooks that enlarged his reputation. Setting up as an abdominal specialist in Wimpole Street, he soon had one of the busiest consulting practices in London. When he was chosen as the subject of a *Spy* cartoon, it was taken also as a compliment to Harley Street.

His name was flashed round the world when in June 1902 he operated at two days' notice on the sixty-year-old King Edward, involving the peremptory postponement of the coronation. London was beflagged, but the attention of the crowds was centred in the bulletin boards on the railings of Buckingham Palace. 'Appendicitis' was on everyone's lips, a new medical term for what was known to doctors as iliac abscess, or perityphlitis, and to the layman as 'inflammation of the bowels'. Treves rejected 'appendicitis' as being 'an uncouth term'. Perityphlitis appeared in the bulletins announcing the operation on the King. Treves confirmed that the 'mysterious little appendix' was a potent mischief-maker, and his caution in the matter of nomenclature was swept aside.

Increasingly endemic in the larger centres of civilization during the previous half century, after the King's operation appendicitis became 'the thing' among the Harley Street class of patient. To have one's appendix taken out was almost a social aspiration, like being presented at Court. There followed much reckless recourse to the knife. The story was told that, as a safeguard, a young woman given to fainting fits carried a card bearing the appeal: 'Please see that my appendix is not removed.'

For the operation on the King, exceptional secrecy was enjoined on the doctors. John Bland-Sutton walked down Queen Anne Street with Treves one evening in June 1902.

'He seemed unusually serious and quiet.' The next day London was agog with the news of the operation. Treves had not spoken a word of it to his fellow surgeon. Those who worked on the case were given numbers and pseudonyms for telegraphic purposes. Treves was number 6, and called 'Mr Turner'. To avoid recognition at Windsor, where there were reporters meeting every train, he wore old clothes, and walked from Slough station to the Castle. He found the King's closest medical adviser, Sir Francis Laking, in tears. The King had sent him out of the sick-room with the pronouncement: 'I am going to London for the coronation at all costs.' His Majesty remained adamant when Treves told him: 'If you go to the Abbey in your present state, you will arrive a corpse.'

The journey to London was made, the King holding his stomach in pain as he bowed to his cheering subjects. Reaching Buckingham Palace, he was in a state of near-collapse. The Buhl Room was hurriedly transformed into an emergency operating theatre. At 12.30 on the afternoon of June 24, 1902, the King was helped into the room, wearing an old dressing-gown of which Queen Alexandra afterwards told Treves she was 'heartily ashamed'. The operation saved the King's life. Fearing post-operative complications, Treves told colleagues that he had no sleep for seven nights. His success made him the most famous surgeon of the decade, and enabled him to retire at the age of fifty-five.

*

The story of 'the elephant man' was one of the strangest in Sir Frederick Treves's casebooks. In 1884, he exhibited to the Pathological Society of London a human monstrosity called John Merrick who had been exploited by travelling showmen on the Continent. When Treves first heard of him, he was being harboured in an empty greengrocer's shop in the Mile End Road. Merrick was a victim of congenital hypertrophy of the bones, and of pachydermatocele and papilloma of the skin. Facially, he was so hideous that he wore a mask. 'At no time had I met with such a degraded or perverted version of a human being,' Treves wrote. The man's forehead was a huge osseous mass, 'like a loaf', that almost occluded one eye. The head circumference equalled that of the waist. Another mass of bone projected from the upper jaw. From the back of the head there hung a fleshy appendage covered by fungoid-like skin. Similar dropsical masses, 'covered by the same loathsome cauliflower skin', hung down the man's back. His only normal feature was his left hand, 'a beautiful hand, which any woman might have envied'.

As related by Treves, John Merrick's reclamation into a limited enjoyment of life was a medical triumph, largely accomplished by skilful nursing, physical and mental. Treves arranged for him to live in a small back room of the hospital. He was visited several times by Queen Alexandra and other persons of high degree, for whom seeing him was a test of nerve as well as a gesture of compassion. Treves even took him to a Drury Lane pantomime.

'A box was obtained. Merrick was brought up in a carriage with drawn blinds and was allowed to make use of the royal entrance. I had begged three of the hospital sisters to don evening dress and to sit in front so as to "dress" the box and to form a screen. Merrick and I occupied the back of the box, which was kept in shadow. All went well, and no one saw a figure, more monstrous than any on the stage, mount the staircase or cross the corridor.'[1]

Treves's humane insight was illustrated again in the case of General Sir John Cowans, the former Quartermaster-General of the British Army, who lay dying of cancer in 1920. His sufferings were described by his wife in letters that have been preserved. 'Give me a bloody revolver!' he begged Treves, the sweat of agony pouring down his face. Treves told the nursing sister: 'See that a bottle of port is put on the bedside table. And give him a pack of cards. It will ease his mind to play with them.' The general died that morning, the port bottle half empty, the playing cards scattered over the bed.

References to his courtly employment were apt to provoke

[1] Sir Frederick Treves: *The Elephant Man* (Cassell, 1923).

Treves to repetitive anecdote in his last years. He enjoyed re-telling the story of an illustrious predecessor of his in the rôle of Serjeant Surgeon, Sir Benjamin Brodie (1783-1862), who was called away just before he was due to lecture to medical students. A notice was displayed on the blackboard indicating that he had been 'commanded to attend Her Majesty'. Beneath the notice an unknown hand chalked in large letters: *God save the Queen.*

From his place of retirement by the lakeside at Geneva, Treves set forth on travels that showed in him the makings of an explorer. He wrote a number of readable travel books, notably *The Other Side of the Lantern.* Contrasting with that attractive account of the life that he had seen in Far Eastern places was his volume on Dorset in the once popular *Highways and Byways* series. When he died (of peritonitis) in 1923, Thomas Hardy was at his funeral. By then, Bertrand Dawson was in the ascendant as a Court physician. It was Treves who had commended him in that quarter.

*

King Edward's operation that had given Sir Frederick Treves public pre-eminence over the potentates, princes, and plenipotentiaries who arrived and departed at the time of the postponed coronation, meant profound disappointment for another member of the royal medical entourage. Not yet forty, Alfred Fripp, of Guy's Hospital and Harley Street, was a Surgeon-in-Ordinary to His Majesty. Yet he knew nothing of the decision to operate until, waiting to cross Parliament Square, he heard an American ask a traffic policeman about the coronation. 'There isn't going to be a coronation,' the policeman announced. 'The King is having an operation today.'

Fripp had been *persona grata* in the Marlborough House circle since the death of the Duke of Clarence, the heir to the Throne, ten years before. He had been the young duke's friend and confidant. He had every reason to expect to be called to the royal bedside; he had been told so by Sir Francis Laking, the King's physician. The summons did not come. Fripp wrote in his diary that he was 'very depressed' and 'very miserable'. Subsequently he wrote: 'Those were very difficult days for me. Everybody wondered why I was left out of the bulletins.' In the same week, he noted 'having to handle four millionaires', including William Waldorf Astor and Sir Alfred Beit. One of them paid him a fee of a thousand guineas. Now it seemed to him that his career was gravely prejudiced.

It was the monarch himself who proved the fear to be groundless. He sent for Fripp and tactfully explained the situation. When Treves had pronounced an operation to be inevitable, the King said to him: 'You will want somebody to help you.' Treves had answered: 'Sir, you don't want the entire College of Surgeons.' Fripp wrote in his diary: 'King Edward was extremely nice about my not being in the case.'

He recorded a conversation with the King in which 'the talk turned on the commercial way of doctors'. They discussed the case of an earl living in Ireland who was a patient of Fripp's, suffering from cancer of the stomach. 'In his last despair, he wrote to a fashionable surgeon asking what his fee would be to come and advise. Ignoring all professional etiquette, and without communicating with me, the surgeon at once dashed off to Ireland, having instructed his secretary to send a telegram: *Have started my fee six hundred guineas whether I operate or not.*' Fripp noted that 'the King had heard of the incident, and was very indignant'.

Berkeley Moynihan's name was mentioned in subsequent recountings of that episode. As an abdominal surgeon, he displayed not a little of the nerve of his father, an Army sergeant who won the V.C. in the Crimea.

III

MORE THAN A BEDSIDE MANNER

'The strain of modern life', a dominant if dubious consulting-room theme at the beginning of the century, was succeeded by a new line of talk in Harley Street: auto-intoxication, intestinal stasis, uric acid poisoning. Psychological medicine was being dismissed as a product of alien imaginations, having no relevance to English anxiety states. *The Interpretation of Dreams*, published in 1900, set up resistances that in some quarters outlasted the widely publicised discussion of 'the significance of the unconscious' in which Jung took a leading part at the meeting of the British Medical Association at Aberdeen in July 1914.[1]

Static electricity was being hopefully proposed as a therapeutic agent in cases of neurasthenia. In 1914, Dr Edwin Ash, 24 Harley Street, proposed its use 'for the relief of neuroses and psycho-neuroses'. Meanwhile, the new mild analgesic drug, aspirin, was being prescribed with increasing frequency. It was dismissed as 'a modern craze' by E. J. Tyrrell, MRCS, LRCP(Lond.), DPH(Camb.).

Even the more majestic seniors of the profession talked of the 'miracles' being performed by the new school of surgeons. With their sterilised rubber gloves, white gowns, caps, and mouth masks, they were like mentors from another planet. A few diehards remained to deplore the march of progress. A colleague of Sir John Bland-Sutton, chief surgeon of Middlesex Hospital, told him of an old Guy's Hospital man whom he had invited to see a leg amputation in which the new aseptic

[1] 'It is refreshing in these times to find a lecture on this subject without allusion to Freud or Jung.' *The Lancet*, 21 September 1918.

techniques were used. At the end of the operation, the former Guy's man confessed that he had 'a fancy for the old methods and liked to see some blood and sawdust about'.

At Edinburgh medical school, Professor 'Tommy' Annandale was still operating in his old chocolate-hued frock coat, 'stiff with coagulated gore'. He was heard to remark: 'They say it doesn't matter how long one washes one's hands, because there will still be organisms in the sweat glands and hair follicles, so I rub *my* hands with vaseline. That should stop the little beggars coming out.'

In 1906, the heartland of private medical practice in England was assailed by the arrows of George Bernard Shaw's wit in *The Doctor's Dilemma*, which had its first night at the Royal Court Theatre, London, on 20 November that year. In the play, Shaw posed one of the 'problems' that he held to be a chief justification of the modern drama. Caricaturing certain types of specialist—recognisably, some playgoers thought, citing Sir Almroth Wright, the eminent bacteriologist, and, mistakenly, by the dramatist's later account, Sir William Arbuthnot Lane, the equally eminent surgeon—Shaw drew ready laughter with his often mischievous fun at the expense of smooth professionalism. As an intellectual exercise, the play did not prejudice the standing of Harley Street in Edwardian society, which, as successive honours lists showed, continued to respect the doctrine of its infallibility.

In spite of the pomposities, the white spats, astrakhan collars, carnation buttonholes, and the virtuoso manipulation of stethoscopes, Harley Street had more to offer than an expensive bedside manner. Sir Bertrand Dawson was telling graduates of London Hospital in no punning mood: 'Never cut out your poor patients.' He himself set the example. Hearing that a commissionaire's daughter was an invalid from birth, and considered incurably so, he undertook to see her without fee. Three times the parents failed to keep the appointment with him in Wimpole Street. Dawson had reason to decline further interest; but he did not exercise it. Finally, the child was brought to him. He traced the source of her illness, which was glandular, and his treatment of the case was entirely successful. There was Sir Douglas Powell, great authority on respiratory diseases, recalled by a correspondent of *The Times*:

'When he was at the height of his popularity, and much overworked, he visited a case every week for many months, knowing that he could do nothing but ease pain and give comfort to the dying invalid and the lonely surviving relative. I cherish a memory of that worn ascetic figure rushing up a long flight of stairs, standing calm and serene with his rare smile by the sick bed as if he had not another patient in the world and then, as soon as the door was closed, hurrying off to another case. It was the custom of this patient, who was by no means wealthy, to have a cheque ready, which was handed to Sir Douglas as he left the house. He stopped one day on the doorstep and said to the relative, "Don't give me any more cheques. I only burn them".'

In his first years at 141 Harley Street, the future Lord Horder saw many of his patients without payment—more than half of them, his son has said. 'Patients were simply marked 0, 1 or 2 in the appointment book and charged that number of guineas accordingly.'[1]

In 1915, the report of a Royal Commission on university education contained the criticism that the typical consultant in and about Harley Street was less concerned with advancing medical knowledge than with improving his bank balance. Patients seeking reassurance could find it in *The Lancet* (founded 1823) and the *British Medical Journal* (1851). Both contained original papers or reprinted clinical lectures by the best brains in the profession. Occasionally, no doubt, a contributed paper was devilled by a younger man only too ready to render that service to the personage whose name, with its panoply of letters-after, appeared over it on the printed page. An impressive number of those contributions bore the ascription 'Harley Street'.

Lay readers, unversed in publishing economics, might have been surprised by the tone of some of the adjacent advertising,

[1] Mervyn Horder: *The Little Genius* (1966)

e.g.: 'The Ethereal Bromo for Brain Workers', 'Iodinized Wine', and 'Trypsin: A New Treatment for Carcinoma'. Abundant editorial proof was available in the columns of both *The Lancet* and the *British Medical Journal* to show that behind the fashionable reputations and the newsworthy names were others whose quality was a matter of private rather than public esteem. 'For although we could do without the adventurers, it is the solid body who do the work, who accept the good, and quietly discard the valueless. These men whose work is often realised only by their near colleagues do invaluable services to mankind.'[1]

Recalling the Harley Street of his early years as a doctor, Ernest Jones, MD, of No 81, who first introduced Freud's concepts and teachings to British medical practice, wrote in his autobiography: 'What a closed corporation, like an expensive club, the consulting world of those days was, where everyone gossiped with the other and looked askance at anyone who was not quite the thing! And many of them were intellectually very inferior people.'

The summit figures were Harley Street men by implication if not by residence. Sir Victor Horsley was at 25 Cavendish Square, Sir Francis Laking at 62 Pall Mall, five minutes' brougham ride from Buckingham Palace. Sir James Reid's consulting-room was at 72 Grosvenor Street, within call of the town houses of some of the wealthiest families in the land, Sir Douglas Powell was at 62 Wimpole Street.

The last three were old school Physicians-in-Ordinary who looked like ambassadors. With their younger colleague, Bertrand Dawson, MD, who had recently left 110 Harley Street for 32 Wimpole Street and who was to eclipse them in fame, they put their signatures to the bulletin announcing the death of Edward VII at 11.50 p.m. on 6 May 1910. Dawson wrote in his notes of the case: 'His Majesty died quite quietly and without struggle.' The public were not to know that for several years the King's doctors had been apprehensive about his recurring bouts of bronchitis.

[1] *Fifty Years of Medicine* (British Medical Association, 1950).

At that time, the most readily recognised names under the dolphin knockers of Harley Street proper were Sir Malcolm Morris, KCVO, FRCS, at No 8, whose services to the community reached beyond his scope as a dermatologist; Sir Anderson Critchett, KCVO, MA, FRCS, ophthalmic surgeon, who could have been mistaken for a French academician, at No. 21; Sir Watson Cheyne, KCMG, FRS, FRCS, at No. 75, man of science and great clinician, who, as Lister's assistant long held fast to the 1 in 20 solution of carbolic acid as the answer to the problems of surgical infection, and who shaved off his beard when he became a later convert to the theory and practice of asepsis; Wilfred Trotter, MD, MS, FRS, at 101, kindred spirit of William James; Hunter Tod, aural surgeon, at 111; and James (afterwards Sir James) Cantlie, MD, specialist in tropical diseases, at 140.

Among indigenous reputations then in the making were those of Charles (later Sir Charles) Gordon Taylor, FRCS, who specialised in cancer excision, at No 15; Richard (in due time, Sir Richard) Cruise, ophthalmic surgeon, at 85; and Thomas Jeeves Horder, MD, whose diagnostic prowess triumphed over the prejudices of contemporaries who deplored his habit of wearing, on summer days, a straw hat with his morning suit.

Orthodoxy was more massively affronted when on 20 February 1911, Mr Justice Darling, in the King's Bench Division of the Royal Courts of Justice, leaned forward to ask the plaintiff in *Thomas v. Barker*: 'Is it the fact that it was one of the doctors who suggested that you bring this action?' There was a glint of expectancy in the judge's eye as he posed the question.

*

Herbert Atkinson Barker (1869–1950) was the son of Thomas Wildman Barker, coroner for south-west Lancashire, who had the possibly unenvied reputation of holding more inquests than any other coroner in the kingdom. On 29 December 1883, after sitting at Lamberhead Green, near Wigan, he genially wished the jurors 'a happy and prosperous

New Year', thanked them for their reciprocal sentiments, and walked to the tramway terminus to return to his office in Wigan. The tram he travelled in ran out of control down a steep incline, Spring Bank. In the resulting crash the coroner was the only fatality. He was the subject of an inquest held the following week.

But for that tragic happening, his only son would probably have worn a barrister's wig. Barker, senior, had cherished that hope. Left to make his own way in life, young Herbert Barker finished his education at Kirkby Lonsdale Grammar School, Westmorland, and went to Canada, partly for the sake of his health, which was far from robust.

On the outward voyage, during a gale, a heavily built passenger slipped and fell on the sloping deck, hurting an arm. Another passenger whom Barker assumed to be a doctor by his prompt professional behaviour, offered first aid. His efforts were of little use. The injured man lay moaning on the deck, convinced that his arm was broken, or his shoulder fractured.

With what he later described as 'a tingling sensation in the fingers', Barker asked if he might intervene. The patient agreeing, Barker knelt beside him, placed his hands on the injured part and shut his eyes as his fingers moved up and down the shaft of the humerus. 'Suddenly I felt that I *knew* what was wrong and how to put it right. The elbow was displaced. I grasped the arm firmly and manipulated it. Looking at the patient's blanched face, I said: "Will you now try to move the arm, sir?" With obvious apprehension, he did so. I had succeeded!'

Daringly, he had applied a technique that he had seen used by a cousin of his, John Atkinson, who practised as a bonesetter in Park Lane, London. It was Herbert Barker's first operation. On its outcome was founded a career that was a triumph of preternatural skill and character. 'Quite surely I knew then that I would sooner or later handle the human skeleton. But first I had to master its secrets, its fulcrums, its levers, its joints and ligaments.' Apart from the fact that his father's death meant that there was no money to help him on his way, he shrank from the sight of blood and was abnormally sensitive to pain. He was unlikely to have qualified as a surgeon.

His time in Canada was short After working for a few months on a farm near Winnipeg, he was back home again with his sisters in Lancashire. Briefly, he indulged a fancy of himself bowing to storms of applause over the footlights. He joined an amateur group at Liverpool, the Sheridan Dramatic Company. Just before his twentieth birthday, he went to London. His cousin Atkinson had undertaken to teach him the bonesetting knack at his Institute of Hygienic Manipulation, at St Paul's House, Wilton Place, S.W. There Atkinson treated a legion of poor patients.

He was a foremost exponent of a skill long practised among the dalesmen of Yorkshire, Cumberland, and Westmorland, and in Devonshire and Cornwall, where wrestling was a traditional sport. The skill was developed by laymen because qualified surgical aid was seldom available in those remote regions. Consequently, a closely guarded arcana of so-called secrets was handed down in certain families.

Those rarely inspired amateurs were an irritating reminder to the medical profession of how little it owed to the law. Anyone could practise medicine, and draw fees for so doing, provided he made no claim to be formally qualified and registered. Anyone could sell a nostrum for any kind of disorder. Anyone could practise bonesetting to the disadvantage of those trained in orthopaedic surgery. Few doctors were willing to accept the inference that there remained a great gap in that branch of medical teaching.

Atkinson had been a ward in Chancery who was educated at King's College, London, and in Paris, studying comparative anatomy and physiology. Up to his time, the best known name among the bonesetters of the United Kingdom was Hutton, a mid-Victorian practitioner who passed on a knowledge of his methods to a qualified medical man, Wharton Hood, of Seymour Street, London. Hood helped Hutton with his numerous non-paying cases. Afterwards, Hood wrote articles for *The*

Lancet on what he had seen and learnt of the bonesetters' craft.

In the 1890s, Atkinson was at his zenith as a West End bonesetter who received cheques for services rendered to three members of the Royal Family and who discreetly made it known that he hoped for a knighthood in return. A man of imposing build, he was prominent among the bluff personalities of the National Sporting Club, where he displayed his prowess as a boxer and wrestler.

Professionally, he relied on finesse where the older bonesetters used brute force. The distinction commended itself to Barker's sensitive temperament. Speaking of Atkinson, he invariably remarked: 'He combined strength with gentleness.' Atkinson's way of communicating his skill to the young man was to say, as he began an examination: 'Here, over mine,' a signal for Barker to place his hands lightly on Atkinson's as he began his diagnosis and treatment. 'I was thus a repository of the knowledge of his methods, indeed, of his whole art'.

Theirs was a refined technique contrasted, for example, with that of the qualified orthopaedic surgeons. Hospital theatres were equipped with iron bars and racks fixed to the walls, and ring-bolts let into the floor, for the attachment of the cords and pulleys used in the reduction of dislocated limbs. Sir John Bland-Sutton, of Middlesex Hospital, where the racks and bars and ring-bolts were in use up to 1895, had as a patient a ship's officer who dislocated his hip during an Atlantic voyage. 'The captain tried to reduce it. As a preliminary, the patient drank half a bottle of brandy and fifty drops of laudanum. Being drunk, he was fastened by a perineal band to a ring-bolt on the deck and ten seamen under the supervision of the captain hauled steadily on the leg. Their efforts were unavailing', and it was the Middlesex Hospital surgeon's task to repair the damage to the patient's muscle and tissue.

*

Barker's first independent practice was in Manchester. He put his name on a door in Grosvenor Street, 'but no patients came. Days passed, and the great public of Cottonopolis left me coldly, severely, miserably alone. The loneliness affected me most grievously.'[1] His situation changed for the better when he cured a patient whose lameness defied the best that a well-known local surgeon, Walter Whitehead, FRCS, could do for him. Whitehead acknowledged Barker's supremacy in the case by sending his nephew as a patient for manipulative treatment, with no less gratifying results. 'Henceforward I was not so terribly alone,' Barker wrote. 'One great, strong-minded, tolerant and famous surgeon was at last on my side.'

He remained *persona non grata* in medical circles. 'Damned quack!' was the phrase relayed to him from 'a well-groomed, ruddy-faced and genial but typically blunt Lancashire doctor'. Another Manchester g.p. made a point of crossing the street when he saw Barker approaching. 'Local members of the faculty had got their knives into me, and did their best to make my position uncomfortable if not untenable.'

Perhaps in reaction from the drabness around him, he formed, early on, an ambition to attract 'a circle of distin-guished patients'. To do that it would be necessary to surround himself with the aura of success, and where else was that more feasible than in London? To London he went. He took a suite of 'really beautiful consulting-rooms' in Suffolk Place, Haymarket, S.W. Like Conan Doyle, who in the same decade put up his plate as an oculist at 2 Devonshire Place, 'close to Harley Street' (rent £120 a year), Barker soon found that he had more than one waiting-room. His capital was small. Crisis came when he was laid low by virulent scarlet fever.

He spent his convalescence in anatomy studies. Then, galled beyond words (his phrase) by his London failure, he returned to Manchester, to pick up the threads of his original practice. Once again, his appointment book was filled with names, chiefly of persons who could not afford more than the smallest fees. When the local press began to notice his activities, reporting his success in mending the injuries of well-known Lancashire sportsmen, he saw that publicity was probably his

[1] Barker: *Leaves From My Life* (1927).

only way to wider recognition. In a not wholly characteristic mood of self-assertion, he told a Manchester chemist named Bellamy: 'I think I shall make a name for myself.'

He went to Glasgow, opened a surgery in Sauchiehall Street, and was astonished that 'patients literally flocked' to his door. Sympathy with unprofessional practice, with its ancient implication of magical powers, was always strong in the farther parts of the kingdom. There were newspaper accounts of 'extraordinary scenes', in which would-be patients came to blows for priority in the queue. Many were the poorest of the poor. He treated them all, regardless of their ability to pay.

In 1904 he travelled south again. John Atkinson had died. For Barker the news was like a call to service. 'The sudden and heavy responsibility of finding myself successor to a man who was so distinguished in his work, weighed upon me.' He soon found that there was no material advantage to him in Atkinson's death. 'His practice was of so personal a nature that his clients practically disappeared at his demise. I saw that I had to make my own position.'

Aware of 'many serious risks, and those not only financial ones', he rented rooms at 72 New Bond Street. London's stipendiary magistrates had been 'making examples' of crystal-gazers and palmists, some of them with Bond Street addresses. Before his first week was out, the police were intervening for quite other reasons. 'Remarkable Scenes in New Bond Street: Wonderful Cures', was a *Daily Express* headline on 5 January 1905. 'Men, women and children with flat feet and "groggy" knees were in such numbers that shoppers were obliged to step into the roadway.' During one weekend, he dealt with 114 cases.

Barker told the reporters: 'I am not a bonesetter—that is really a misnomer. My work is the adjustment of joints, muscles and tendons by a long practised use of the hands. The knife is used too often unnecessarily in these cases.' By 1907, he had so many patients that he was able to take over John Akinson's rooms at Hamilton House, Park Lane, where he put up the well-polished brass name plate that he had brought from Manchester.

To the Editor of *Reynolds' Weekly News*:

Sir,—I desire to certify to the facts which follow. On January 16, a schoolmaster was kept under strong anaesthetics for a space of three hours, and was subjected by a qualified medical practitioner to treatment for a displaced knee cartilage. The operation failed entirely.

On the following Tuesday I attended by invitation at the house of Mr H. A. Barker of 12A Park Lane. There the patient mentioned was operated upon in the presence of myself and a qualified surgeon by Mr Barker, and the cartilage was replaced in less than three minutes. The subject, who had been unable to put more than one foot to the ground, and whose knee was grotesquely deformed when he arrived, was enabled to walk with freedom, and has since reported the condition of the limb to be entirely normal.

I write in the knowledge that this branch of the healing art has been neglected by the medical profession.

London, E.C.   DAVID CHRISTIE MURRAY[1]

Through the London press, Barker made it known that he would show any qualified medical man his method of remedying flat feet, knee cartilage displacements, and convex curvature of the spine in certain age groups. The demonstration was subject to the proviso that the patients had recently been under orthodox treatment. His challenge was ignored. He then invited medical witnesses to study his methods and follow up cases. Four doctors showed interest. One of them was F. W. Axham, MRCS (Lond.), LRCP (Edin.), then in practice at 31 Glasshouse Street, Regent Street, W.

Dr Axham had qualified in the '70s, serving at first as a surgeon in the Army under General Gordon. Sailing home from the Far East, he voluntarily took the place of the ship's doctor who died of yellow fever. With a devotion that earned him official commendation, he tended sixty other cases among passengers and crew. Subsequently, and for many years, he

[1] A well-known journalist and author of the day.

'attended to and alleviated the sufferings of the sick poor', under the aegis of the Westminster Board of Guardians, whose minute books record his 'long and faithful service'.

He was present at forty-five consecutive sessions in Barker's consulting-room. Barker recalled: 'The closeness of his scrutiny was almost disconcerting. He did not praise or condemn, belittle or uphold, what he saw of my manipulations. His attitude was judicially non-committal.' He heard patients crying out in pain, saw others stuff handkerchiefs into their mouths for fear of doing so.

Having seen what he wished to see, Dr Axham paid a formal call on Barker, addressed him approvingly on the work he was doing, and offered his services as anaesthetist. Barker wrote: 'He considered that I was being unfairly and unnecessarily handicapped by not having my patients anaesthetised, and concluded by stating that he believed it to be his duty to assist me in making my manipulations painless.' When Barker asked him whether he was 'prepared to face the storm', Axham answered that 'the paramount duty of my profession is to relieve suffering. You must have an anaesthetist.' Barker was 'greatly moved'. From then on, he wrote 'gas' in brackets against most of his appointments.

Towards the end of 1909, Dr Axham gave gas in Barker's rooms to an ex-medical student, Charles Rowley Thomas, a solicitor's son, crippled by a swimming accident at Shrewsbury School, eight years earlier. He went to Barker as 'a last hope', after being treated unsuccessfully by the surgeons of Charing Cross Hospital, where he had been a student. He had since abandoned his pursuit of a medical career, and was working in the publishing office of Ouseley & Co., at 225 Strand.

Examining Charles Rowley Thomas's knee, Barker saw that it was beyond his kind of skill, that it was probably tuberculous, which meant the knife. He suggested that Thomas should see a Harley Street surgeon. Thomas's response to that advice was: 'I'm fed up with surgeons.' He begged Barker to make a closer examination. Employing Axham as the anaesthetist, Barker did so. Hoping no doubt to rid himself of a difficulty, he recommended a course of radiant heat treatment at a Chelsea nursing home.

Three months afterwards, Thomas's leg was amputated at forty-eight hours' notice, allegedly a life-saving operation. He sued Barker for £5,000 damages, claiming that during the examination under gas Barker had forcibly manipulated the knee which, as a consequence, had flared up into a state involving amputation. Barker was deeply disturbed by the prospect of appearing in a court of law. A man of delicately balanced nerves and of a brooding disposition, he was weighed down by the knowledge that the sympathy of the medical faculty in general was on the plaintiff's side. Looking back from twenty years after, he wrote: 'I shudder even now at the recollection of this tragedy in my career—the sinister combination of circumstances.'

The lawsuit filled three days of the third week in February 1911. Playing it up for its 'human interest', the newspapers made it a *cause célèbre*, with Sir Edward Clarke, KC appearing for the plaintiff, Sir Edward Carson, KC for the defence. Giving evidence, Barker was obviously under strain. His slightly sombre good looks were enhanced by remarkably blue eyes, his most immediately noticeable feature. His voice had attractive overtones softened by a natural diffidence that was apparent from his ordeal in the witness box. While his personality suggested hidden strength, his demeanour was proof that crude self-assertion was alien to his temperament. He had an artist's hands. At times they gripped the edge of the witness box as if he was clinging to a rock in a stormy sea.

He told the court that he had warned Thomas 'in the plainest language' that he could offer no hope of a cure. It was at Thomas's insistence that the second examination was carried out. Dr Axham gave gas. It was the most vital disclosure made during the case, which gave Mr Justice Darling fewer chances than he may have hoped for of asserting his reputation as a wit. We can imagine him, bony-faced, lean as a jockey, listening with feline alertness for the opportunity to make a quotable epigram. 'That is what they call nowadays preventive detention,' he remarked briskly when Sir Edward Carson described the process of enscapulation in medical terms. The comment evoked respectful grins, but not the parenthetical 'laughter in court' that so often punctuated newspaper reports of Darling's cases.

Herbert Waterhouse, MD, FRCS, of 81 Wimpole Street, was named as 'one of the doctors' allegedly in league with Thomas against Barker. A sister of the plaintiff was cross-examined on the point by Carson for the defence.

Q. I do not know whether you would be able to tell us or not as to which of the doctors it was that suggested this action should be brought?

A. It was suggested all round.

Q. Give 'all round' a name. Was it Mr Waterhouse?

A. Yes, I think so.

Q. It was Mr Waterhouse who suggested it?

A. And others.

Q. When did Mr Waterhouse see your brother first?

A. At the end of March, I think.

Q. Did he ever see him between the 26th January and the end of March?

A. I forget.

Q. How soon after he saw him did he suggest an action?

A. At once, I think.

Examined by Sir Edward Clarke, for the plaintiff, Waterhouse was asked: Is it the fact that you were the person who suggested the bringing of an action in this case?

A. It is certainly not. I admit that I did not discourage the bringing of an action.

The special jury was out for fifty-two minutes on 22 February. Asked by the Court Associate: 'Gentlemen, are you all agreed?' the foreman answered, 'Yes.' They had found for the plaintiff. 'What damages?' The foreman announced: 'Twenty guineas—that is, twenty-one pounds.' It was the amount paid to Barker by Thomas in fees.

*

Walter Whitehead, the Manchester surgeon who was by then a past President of the British Medical Association, noted 'with discomfort' that Sir Edward Carson had observed in court that 'if Mr Barker had been a qualified man this action would never have been brought'. Whitehead wrote to Barker warning him: 'You will have to live down the stigma of the trial without getting the credit of your successes. Every member of our jealous profession will make whatever use he can of everything against you, without giving you credit for anything in your favour.' Had he been called upon for an opinion, the surgeon added, he could 'easily have proved that the putrefactive changes which led to the amputation could have been accounted for by other hands than yours'.

The jury's award, it was generally agreed, was the moral equivalent of the derisive farthing damages. For Barker, there was a less satisfactory implication—costs amounting to £3,000.

Immediately after the trial, *The Times* published an article, filling more than two columns, in which the paper's medical correspondent sketched the history of bonesetting as a craft, and surveyed its contemporary applications. Readers were left with the inference that the victims of certain types of disablement and deformity were exposed to the risks of treatment by a horde of humbugs. The medical profession did not adopt the practices of the bonesetters because of 'a well-founded and deeply-rooted distrust of their work . . . The bonesetter in the long run must go.'

Barker replied that some of his patients came to him from orthopaedic hospitals, from which a proportion of them had been discharged as incurable. 'If I were not restrained by a knowledge of human fallibility, including my own, and by a wise law of libel, I could a tale unfold . . . But recrimination takes us no further along the path of progress.' Recognising the existence of 'impudent frauds and charlatans who trade on the reputations of men like Hutton and Atkinson', he asked that the methods of manipulative surgery should be incorporated in the curricula of the medical teaching schools. (*The Times*, 15 March 1911.)

A month later, Dr Axham received a letter from the Registrar of the General Medical Council. 'Information has been laid that you, by your presence, countenance, advice and co-operation have knowingly assisted an unqualified person, named H. A. Barker.' The Medical Defence Union, 4 Trafalgar Square, W.C. had formally drawn the Council's attention to Axham's collaboration with Barker, and had asked that an inquiry concerning it should be held, 'under the terms of the Medical Act, 1858'.

Dr F. W. Axham to the Registrar of the
General Medical Council:

Morden,
Dollis Park,
Church End,
Finchley.
March 23, 1911.

Sir,—I have reached the age of 71, and for fifty years have upheld the status of the profession. At the same time, I admit that medical laws were made to be observed, and that in ordinary cases it is right that they should be.

In the instance of Mr Barker, about whom exception has been taken, I had, previously to associating myself with him, abundant proof of his natural talent and special ability, and, having regarded his work as necessary to the welfare of the community, consented to administer anaesthetics to relieve suffering.

There are thousands willing to bear testimony to benefits received through Mr Barker's agency. Whatever action may be taken against me, my defence lies in the following:

Medical men in practice, specialists, men attached to the Services, persons of rank and distinction, and a host of celebrities, have sought the help of Mr Barker, having failed to obtain relief elsewhere.

Yours faithfully,
F. W. AXHAM

Axham might have made much of his having been at Barker's side for the past five years without being called to account. He did not exaggerate Barker's successes. They could not be exaggerated, for they were outstanding as demonstrations of a rare ability. One of his recent patients was the son of the Surgeon-General of the Royal Navy; another, young Archibald Sinclair,[1] an Etonian who had worn leg-irons in childhood and who was still partly crippled by a congenital defect of the feet. His guardian, Archdeacon William Sinclair, wrote to Barker from St Paul's Cathedral: 'You will have heard that Archie got into Sandhurst. It is a wonderful cure' (2 January 1909). Barker restored to normal activity an Army officer's daughter, Betty Kinloch, chair-ridden for two and a half years after 'some of the most distinguished surgeons in the land' had prescribed medications, baths, sea voyages, graduated exercises, a specially constructed bed, and a spinal corset: 'a much talked-of case'—*London Opinion*, 5 March 1910. W. T. Stead wrote in his *Review of Reviews*: 'I have a young man in my office who has been lame since childhood. He had been under treatment at St Thomas's and other hospitals, without any relief. Mr Barker enabled him to put his foot square to the ground the first time in twenty years.' Doctors called in to treat injuries received at polo by a son of the popular boys' story-writer, R. M. Ballantyne, warned him that he would probably have to resign his commission in the Army. That prognosis was discounted by Barker's extraordinary powers.

A feature of his correspondence files were the letters of appreciation, many of deeply felt gratitude, from sportsmen and athletes. Among them were the captains of both the Oxford and Cambridge University football clubs. The managers of famous professional teams thanked him for the promptitude with which he restored players to the field. There was hardly a leading club, professional and amateur, that did not seek his services. During the football season of 1907–8, he operated on 300 players, most of them suffering from displaced knee cartilages.

In the file of letters handed to his counsel before the lawsuit

[1] Afterwards Sir Archibald Sinclair, some time Secretary of State for Air; later Lord Thurso.

was one from the Midland District of the National Union of Gasworkers and General Labourers: 'W. Thorne, MP, general secretary, Arthur Hayday, district secretary' (well-known names in British trades union history). Quaintly addressing Barker as 'Dearest Sir,' it informed him: 'We, the members of the Bulwell No 3 Branch of the above Union, desire to tender our sincere thanks to you for the kind consideration and attention given to our comrade E. W. Powell that has been under your treatment. I have seen him since his return and he is simply a miracle. I am, Sir, yours truly, R. COOPER.'

The headmaster of Shirley Schools, near Croydon, J. F. H. Roberts, had been sorely beset many years by complications arising from an ankle injury. He was treated by three qualified surgeons, who, he wrote, 'inflicted me with valgus plates, steel arched socks, rubber pads, elongated heels, surgical boots, etc., none of which gave any relief'. He had turned to Barker 'in despair'. In a few weeks he could walk '20 to 30 miles without distress', and his letter sends out its message of gratitude these fifty years after.

Another telling document was the testimony of R. B. Robertson, a clerk in the Principal Probate Registry, Somerset House, London. 'Somewhere about November 1906, I sadly came to the conclusion that all games were at an end for me. A succession of sprains had left my leg weak and painful, with the arch of my right foot sprained and dropped. Walking had become a great difficulty, until I was reduced occasionally to going out on my hands and knees.' Obtaining no relief from the doctors, he yielded to suggestions that he should see Barker. After five treatments, he was delivered from his disablement. 'My life has been changed by you,' he wrote. 'No more hobbling about in pain! On my 24th birthday I feel I am making a new start in life.'

The Marchioness of Exeter wrote from Burghley House, Stamford, to *The Times*: 'Whilst running down a steep hill I displaced the cartilage of my left knee. After this, the joint was a continual source of trouble to me.' She saw a number of

Harley Street men. 'They were unable to help', beyond fitting her knee with an unsightly wire-gauze cage. Consulting Barker after eighteen years of pain, 'he at once diagnosed what was wrong, and after gas had been given the cartilage was put in place. I can now play tennis, dance, etc., without any support whatever, and in perfect comfort' (14 February 1911).

*

On 26 April 1911, the Registrar of the General Medical council wrote to Dr Axham informing him that a charge against him of 'infamous conduct in a professional respect' was to be heard at a meeting of the Council at 299 Oxford Street, London, on 24 May. It would then be decided 'whether or not they should direct your name to be removed from the Medical Register'.

Axham believed that Herbert Waterhouse, the Wimpole Street surgeon who had given evidence against Barker in the recent lawsuit, had a family link with the legal firm of Waterhouse & Co., then of New Court, Lincoln's Inn, who acted for the General Medical Council. There was in fact no such connection. In an unpublished letter, Axham asserted that 'Mr Waterhouse has felt the result of Mr Barker's handiwork in the way of diminished receipts for operations on cartilage cases, and so resolved to damage Barker through me'. Barker had obviated a fee of 200 guineas being paid for a proposed surgical operation on the knee of a well-known sportsman, believed to have been O. T. Norris, of Oxford University football fame, who was also a cricket 'blue'. Barker pronounced the opinion that the knife was quite unnecessary. He enabled the patient to return to the playing fields without recourse to it. In another letter, Axham spoke of Waterhouse as 'the hostile gentleman'.

Axham was not a man of malicious intent. He had all the attributes of 'the beloved physician' of popular fancy; the gentle, reflective manner, the utter trustworthiness, the goodness of heart. Herbert Waterhouse became the highly respected senior surgeon at Charing Cross Hospital, to which he gave years of devoted service and where he is affectionately remembered. His work during the First World War earned him a knighthood. It was his custom every Friday, after finishing his operation list at the hospital, to take tea and crumpets at the Savage Club, where he delighted in the company of creative men in literature and the arts.

On 16 May 1911, Axham received a letter from Waterhouse & Co., reminding him of 'the disabilities which follow the erasure of a name from the Medical Register'. Towards the end of the month, he attended at 299 Oxford Street to appear before the nineteen members of the Disciplinary Committee of the General Medical Council, where 'he was treated in an off-hand way', according to a friend of his, the Rev. J. L. Walton, MA, vicar of All Saints, Southend-on-Sea, who accompanied him. 'He was told that two cases were to be disposed of before he would be called. He therefore requested the accommodation of a chair, but was informed that all the chairs were in use. As a result, he was under the obligation of pacing a corridor for upwards of an hour.'

The proceedings in the hall of judgement were 'painfully brief' (Walton). He was asked: 'Are you prepared to dissociate yourself from Mr Barker?' When he answered: 'No', one of the thirty-four members of the Council, evidently hard of hearing, called out: 'What does he say?' The president, Sir Donald MacAlister, KCB, made it clear: 'He declines to dissociate himself from Mr Barker,' and asked Dr Axham to retire.

Recalled after a quarter of an hour, he was told by the president: 'Dr Axham, I have to inform you that the Council have judged you to have been guilty of infamous conduct, and have directed the Registrar to erase from the Medical Register the name of Frederick William Axham.' With a polite bow, Axham left the hall, a professionally discredited man. As he walked away, he was heard to say to himself: 'Infamous conduct—infamous conduct!' as if he could not believe what he had heard. His incredulity remained with him to the end of his days.

It was an added misfortune for him that he was 'struck off' on the same day as two doctors who were serving prison sentences: inevitably, casual readers of the newspapers linked his offence with theirs. They at least had a right of appeal to the civil courts that had convicted them. For Dr Axham there was no hope of redress unless he conformed to the demands of the General Medical Council.

After just on a half century of honourable practice, he was peremptorily deprived of his standing as a medical man. A letter of 25 May confirmed that the act of erasure had been carried out. 'I cannot but regret', he wrote, 'that after 49 years' work, the profession should deem me unworthy to be further connected with it because I have helped a man to more mercifully perform a service which has done much to relieve suffering, and which must, sooner or later, be recognised by the surgical world.'

The case was a landmark in medical history, one that is well within recall by many adult memories. If it did not produce an effect comparable with that of the great epidemics, which tended to diminish faith in the doctors, it lost the medical hierarchy considerable respect, and created a certain unease in the public mind. People felt that to the General Medical Council unorthodoxy, rather than quackery, was the evil that had to be vanquished.

As the *British Medical Journal* was to point out to a later generation of its readers, 'the history of bonesetting seems to have been ignored by the General Medical Council when it struck Dr Axham off the *Register* in 1911'.[1] St Bartholomew's Hospital in the long ago had on its staff a surgeon bonesetter and an assistant in the same category, posts that subsequently lapsed. In 1867, Sir James Paget warned readers of the *Journal* that if the bonesetter 'can cure a case which you have failed to cure, his fortune may be made and yours marred'.

At the same time, much of the criticism of the Council was based on an imperfect understanding of its functions. Origin-

[1] 29 July 1950.

ally known as the General Council of Medical Education and
Registration of the United Kingdom, it consists of forty-seven
members, of whom eight, including three laymen, are nomin-
ated by the Queen, with the advice of her Privy Council or the
Governor of Northern Ireland. Eleven other members are
elected by the postal votes of the profession in England, Wales,
Scotland, and Ireland (including the Republic). The remain-
ing twenty-eight members represent each of the universities
which grant medical degrees, the various Royal Colleges in
London, Edinburgh, Glasgow, and Dublin, the Society of
Apothecaries of London, and the Apothecaries' Hall of
Dublin.

The Council is a statutory body set up under the Medical
Act, 1858, to ensure the maintenance of an adequate standard
of technical training in the medical schools, and to compile
the Medical Register, which records the names of all who have
undertaken the prescribed training courses, and who have
satisfactorily passed the qualifying examinations. Under
Section 29 of the Medical Act, the Council is also a penal and
disciplinary body with the power to remove from the Register
the name of any qualified practitioner who fails to conform
to its standards.

For many years after the Act was passed, unqualified persons were engaged by doctors as assistants. Mostly they were
employed to look after the midwifery and Poor Law cases.
The arrangement was professionally known as 'covering'. It
did not come under the ban of the General Medical Council
until the end of the nineteenth century. Then, all registered
practitioners received the official reminder that 'any doctor
who knowingly enables or assists a person not duly qualified
and registered as a medical practitioner, to practise medicine
or to treat patients in respect of matters requiring medical or
surgical discretion or skill, becomes liable to disciplinary
proceedings'.[1]

Dr Axham acknowledged the rule and his transgression of

[1] General Medical Council: *Functions, Procedure, and Disciplinary
Jurisdiction.*

IV

WAR COMES TO HARLEY STREET

'We hear it often said of the medical profession that new discoveries are met by captious criticism and ungenerous mistrust,' Sir Douglas Powell reminded those who heard his Harveian Oration at the Royal College of Physicians. Medical conservatism laughed at the theory of the circulation of the blood. It dismissed the stethoscope and the laryngoscope as 'physiological toys'. It rejected the use of chloroform as impious. Lister was scoffed at for his allegiance to Pasteur, who had no medical degree. The same large reserves of prejudice were marshalled against the open-air treatment for tuberculosis, ovariotomy, hypnosis, massage, physiotherapy, and plastic surgery.

As Sir Douglas Powell was careful to say, 'new knowledge should be proved; and too facile acceptance can be wished for only by promulgators of error'. In the matter of the 'bloodless surgery' of Herbert Barker, the public was expected to abide by the dictum of the medical hierarchy that an unauthorised practitioner could not know anything worth knowing. Barker was an intuitive worker—'so what?' in effect asked a writer in the *Medical Press*. 'He cannot acquire a knowledge of anatomy, physiology, pathology, and morbid anatomy, by intuition, nor by that means become an expert diagnostician.'

Taunted in the *British Medical Journal* with the question, Why don't you qualify? Barker answered: 'I do not qualify in medicine because I have no wish to practise medicine.' He did not care to waste his time, he said, in studying techniques that for his purposes were irrelevant and inadequate. He asked: 'Supposing I had gone to some medical school and secured a diploma, how would it have affected the worth of the methods I have employed with success during the years I have been in practice?'

The term 'manipulative surgery', which he claimed to have originated, was distasteful to the qualified surgeons, who went on calling him a bonesetter. They forgot that there was a time when they in turn were condescendingly regarded by the physicians, who classed them with bonesetters and blood-letters. They took exception to his empirical methods and the limited field in which he exercised his skill, pointing out that the qualified surgeon must be physician, anatomist, bacteriologist. The implication appeared to be that skill such as his would be welcomed but only if it were substantiated by the traditional five years' medical course. For the time being, critical feelings were appeased by the publication in November 1911 of a Blue Book, *The Practice of Medicine and Surgery by Unqualified Persons* (HMSO, Cd. 5422). Data for it was supplied by medical officers of health, who showed scanty respect for the activities of local bonesetters.

The Blue Book reported numerous complaints made against the trespass by bonesetters into the domain of qualified orthopaedic surgeons; that the number of bonesetters was increasing; that an 'astonishing amount' of public confidence was placed in them; that Friendly Societies in the North of England were even accepting their accident certificates as being equal in value to those of the doctors; and that 'irretrievable harm' was being done. The impression was given of a considerable part of the population, 'largely working class and in many cases illiterate and uneducated', exposed to the ministrations of inexpert practitioners.

Barker's great champion in the public domain was W. T. Stead, who arraigned the doctors in an eight-page article in the *Review of Reviews*, insisting that the time had come for them to see to it that 'this fooling should cease'. T. P. O'Connor, MP took a similarly strong line in the magazine named after him. An article in the *English Review* on *Bonesetting and the*

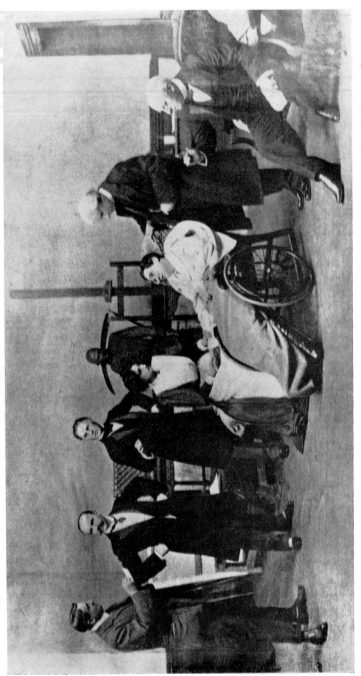

The Doctor's Dilemma. A scene from the original Royal Court Theatre production in 1906. Shaw's famous play made fun of certain Harley Street personages and attitudes.

Dr F. W. Axham, struck off the Medical Register for 'infamous conduct', namely, giving anaesthesia to Sir Herbert Barker's patients.

Sir Herbert Barker, the unqualified manipulative surgeon, whose long running battle with the General Medical Council is part of medical history.

Faculty[1] by Walter Whitehead, FRCS had a powerful effect on non-medical opinion. He quoted a letter from a fellow practitioner, George Garrard, MRCS, LRCP, of St Leonards-on-Sea, whose undergraduate son, after treatment by Barker, announced: 'I was never able to walk so well before.' General practitioners everywhere were startled by that authoritative endorsement of the methods of one whom their professional journals treated as a charlatan. Barker himself was uplifted. 'The Faculty cannot ignore Mr Whitehead or shut their eyes to the defence of manipulative surgery which he has made.'

His satisfaction was echoed by Dr Axham, who believed that the General Medical Council would not bring retribution on Whitehead, 'whose record is too strong for them'. In the same letter, Dr Axham expressed appreciation of the support given to him by John Murray, of Albermarle Street, W. 'I value it beyond words'. The distinguished publisher had written to the *Daily Mail*: 'As a magistrate, I had ample opportunities of knowing Dr Axham and his work when he was medical officer of the Union Infirmary, Poland Street, W. I formed the highest opinion of his integrity, his professional skill, and his judgment in very difficult circumstances. That he should be accused of "infamous conduct" seems to me not only incredible, but entirely discreditable to those who make the charge' (8 December 1911).

The Times printed a letter from Robert Shewan, of Shewan, Tomes & Co, 27 Leadenhall Street, E.C. reciting the benefit he had received at Barker's hands with Axham's help. 'Nearly twenty years ago, in Hong Kong, I broke both my ankles. I was assured by the doctors there that nothing could be done for me, and that I would be a cripple for life. I then went home to England, but fared no better. Among others, I consulted Mr Wharton-Hood [orthopaedic surgeon, 11 Seymour Street, Portman Square], who told me there was nothing to be done.' He had to walk thereafter in boots with an iron plate in the soles, 'without which I could only stagger across the room'.

[1] *English Review*, July 1911. *The Lancet* refused an advertisement of the issue containing the article.

He was seen by Barker, who manipulated his dislocated bones under gas given by Axham. 'I can now put my feet to the ground without fear of pain, and walk with the greatest pleasure and comfort' (18 December 1911).

Shortly afterwards, Dr Axham received notice that he was to be deprived of his 'rights and privileges' as a Licentiate of the Royal College of Physicians of Edinburgh. In that new crisis in his affairs he was befriended by James McKay, solicitor, of 26 Queen Street, Edinburgh, to whom Barker wrote on 19 April 1912: 'I can never be sufficiently grateful to you for your ready help concerning Dr A. You must allow me to do something in return. I've lost one of my best friends through that awful "Titanic" affair—Mr W. T. Stead. It is all too shocking for words.' McKay wrote to Barker: 'There can be no manner of doubt that it is not poor Dr Axham that the proceedings are levelled against, but against your good self' (7 May 1912).

Appealing to the Registrar of the Royal College at Edinburgh, Axham asked: 'Supposing a man were to perfect a means of curing cancer, *beyond any possibility of doubt*, and the treatment could only be applied by its experienced discoverer, under anaesthesia, would you proscribe, by striking off the Register, any practitioner who rendered such treatment painless by the administration of an anaesthetic? This *precisely* exemplifies my position with regard to Mr Barker.' He begged the College to hesitate 'before deciding to treat me with further indignity, in the exceptional circumstances of this particular case'.

On 7 May 1912, the College confirmed Dr Axham's suspension *sine die*. Likewise resorting to analogy, the then head of the Pelman Institute wrote to Barker: 'It is just as if a Salvation Army captain had discovered in Palestine a new Sinai Codex that completely changed the interpretation of a part of the Greek Testament, but which an Anglican parson refused to recognise because the Salvation Army captain had not been episcopally ordained.'

*

Publicity was more essential to Barker's propaganda than to his livelihood. He courted it with some persistence, and not always wisely, to the detriment of his position in the eyes of the medical die-hards. The *Daily Express*, the *Daily Mail*, and *Truth* kept the controversy alive through the menacing years of 1912–13. He was specially appreciative of the crusading persistence of 'Labouchère's old paper', which pronounced the opinion that 'he is probably doing more to relieve suffering humanity than any living surgeon'.

Possibly more directly influential in assisting the process by which Harley Street became the centre of a less preposterous orthodoxy was the leading article in *The Times* on 7 November 1912, headed 'What is A Quack?' As *Truth* remarked, 'a great many old readers, especially in the neighbourhood of Harley Street and Cavendish Square, must have rubbed their eyes on reading it'. The leading article brought prominent medical personages as disputants in the public arena. It was followed by an appeal in the paper for 'a more liberal spirit in a profession which rightly enjoys great privileges'.

What the demi-gods of medicine did not know was that Barker had successfully treated an assistant editor of *The Times*, J. B. Capper, after fifteen years of lameness from knee cartilage displacement. Thereafter no chance was missed of giving him favourable notice in the paper. One of its leading articles referred to him as 'a benefactor of the public who ought to be honoured accordingly'.

His letter files show that in those years his skill was impressing a growing number of medical men. Some consulted him about personal disabilities, others were passing their patients on to him; for example, H. Valentine Knaggs, LRCP, MRCS of 25 Wimpole Street: 'I want to send you a man whose case has been badly bungled by the ornaments of the profession.' The medical officer of Charterhouse School, Dr C. W. Haig-Brown, wrote privately: 'I never feel the slightest hesitation in recommending patients with lame joints (of whom I see many) to consult Mr Barker. I find that he always does them good.' A future Home Secretary, W. Joynson Hicks, MP (later

Lord Brentford) wrote to tell Barker that his son, unsuccessfully treated by Dr Vernon Jones, of Arlington Street, W., was at last pronounced fit by the Army doctors—'which is, I think, the best testimony to your cure' (18 September 1914).

Barker himself suffered at that time a spinal wrench with obscure effects that troubled him for the next fifteen years. He was unable to reach the site of it—'the tenth, eleventh, and twelfth dorsal vertebrae'—with his own healing hands, and no one of comparable powers could be found to treat it for him.

*

Familiar and famous figures disappeared from the Harley Street scene in the autumn of 1914. With them went the last of the surgeons' carriages-and-pairs and the physicians' Victorias and broughams. The rattle of hooves and wheels on the mews' cobblestones of Harley Place and Welbeck Way would be heard no more. Instead of top hats and white spats, there was a strange blooming of maroon lapel tabs and hat-bands, often adorning uniforms so ill-fitting as to suggest that they had been hired rather than bespoke. Middle-aged doctors, gazetted as temporary lieutenants at 24s. a day (2s. a day extra for ear specialists, 4s. a day extra for oculists), were seen furtively avoiding the salutes to which they were entitled from the lower orders.

Sir Almroth Wright looked no more than every other inch a colonel, the rank in which he was gazetted on his appointment as consulting physician to the Forces overseas, with Alexander Fleming, FRCS, temporary captain, RAMC, as his assistant. As one of the most distinguished members of the profession, Sir Bertrand Dawson looked even more so in uniform. Sir Watson Cheyne, Sir Alfred Fripp, and Humphrey Rolleston (knighted later), were appointed consultants to the Royal Navy, the first two with the rank of Surgeon Rear-Admiral. Fripp, that well-favoured man, declined rank and pay, determined to retain his freedom of access to high authority with no red-tape hindrances. It enabled him to press for reforms with a vigour that would have been discountenanced had he worn uniform. John (afterwards Sir John) Bland-Sutton was attached to the 3rd London General Hospital, Wandsworth, as a captain, RAMC, content with that modest rank 'in order to obtain practical experience of gunshot wounds'. Sir William Arbuthnot Lane, like Dawson, one of the first medical men commissioned in Haldane's new Territorial Force in 1908, was appointed consultant to the Aldershot command.

'The war was a terrible experience', he wrote retrospectively. 'The first evidence I had of its probable immediate onset was that, on the occasion of the International Congress in 1914, we had invited many of the prominent German and Austrian surgeons to dinner. They, with the exception of Eiselsberg, notified us that they had been recalled to their own countries, Eiselsberg remaining longer than they.' More explicitly stated, the occasion was the meeting in London that July of the Clinical Congress of Surgeons of North America, at which Professor von Eiselsberg, of Vienna, was to give an address on stomach ulcers.

For Arbuthnot Lane, the war at least meant the end of the controversial harassments in which he had been plunged as the protagonist of colectomy, the 'big operation' that he had devised for the relief of chronic intestinal stasis and the manifold ills that he attributed to it. He had been under heavy attack at the several sessions of the Royal Society of Medicine in 1913. According to T. B. Layton, a Harley Street colleague, he drove away from the last of them 'quite crushed'.

*

For another noted surgeon, Sir Victor Horsley, of 25 Cavendish Square, the war did not mean instant translation to a new and exciting field of action. At the age of fifty-seven, he had one of the great medical reputations at home and abroad. He also had many stern critics, if more admiring friends. His democratic sympathies and his rigid temperance views roused influential opposition. For him, alcohol was 'racial poison', and the brewers enemies of the people. His contributions to medical science were important enough to gain him the Fellowship of the Royal Society.

They began with his experiments, as house surgeon at University College Hospital, London, in recording the effects of self-administered chloroform. 'Not many of us would care to do what Horsley did', one of his contemporaries wrote. 'He anaesthetised himself, or got a friend to anaesthetise him, it is said about fifty times in all, and he devised many ways of signalling his experiences.'[1] It was brave work, its risks undertaken in the hope of perfecting the means by which operations could be done without excessive haste. Formerly, surgeons had to be swift with the knife, to avoid protracted pain.

A professor of pathology before he became a professor of clinical surgery, Horsley was the chief interpreter in England of Pasteur's ideas, and it was his work on rabies that resulted in its virtual extinction in the British Isles. 'The most awful of all diseases', was his verdict after seeing it at close quarters; his laboratory attendant died from it. He founded the modern study of the thyroid gland. As surgeon to the National Hospital for the Paralysed and Epileptic, Queen Square, W.C., he was in the forefront of researches that put cerebral surgery on a surer basis than before. His knowledge of the physiology of the brain was not surpassed by any other living surgeon. 'He erected the new department of neurological surgery.'[2]

He did his first brain operation at the National Hospital on 25 May 1886. The patient, a Scot aged twenty-two, was run over in a street accident when a boy. His injuries included a compound fracture of the skull and loss of brain tissue. He became the victim of continuous fits. A record kept in his first two weeks at the hospital showed a total of 2,870 seizures. Horsley diagnosed 'scar involving the hinder end of the superior frontal sulcus'. He removed the scar to a depth of two centimetres. The wound healed well, the patient's mental state improved, the fits ceased. It was a remarkable demon-

[1] Stephen Paget: *Sir Victor Horsley* (1919).
[2] Sir Charles Ballance's testimony at the Royal College of Surgeons, December 1921.

stration of flair and skill at a period in medical history when the brain was *terra incognita* to surgical explorers. By the end of the year, Horsley had carried out ten difficult and exacting brain operations, with one failure.

'To watch Horsley operate on a brain case was a stimulating experience', Sir James Purves-Stewart, MD, wrote in his reminiscences, *Sands of Time*. 'It took him only a few minutes to make a window in the skull, amid a shower of bony splinters. Once within the cranium, he was swift yet cautious. The very speed of his operations spared his patients a considerable degree of surgical shock which, in those days, sometimes followed the work of slower operators.'

*

On 9 June 1887, Horsley undertook the first operation of its kind known to medical science, the removal of a tumour from the spinal cord. The patient was a Regular Army officer, Captain Gilbey, whose anguish through three years was so intense that he was brought to the verge of insanity. Bodily functions were out of action, while every movement, however slight, meant often excruciating pain for the patient, whose long-drawn moaning alternated with screams unnerved the younger nurses looking after him. Seen in consultation by Sir William Gowers, Sir William Jenner, and Dr Percy Kidd, he told them: 'I need immediate help—an end to this torture!' Agreeing, fearfully, to one more examination, he was rolled on to his side, crying out with the inevitable pain of it.

As Sir William Jenner's fingers moved up the vertebrae, the patient's groans echoed through the house, from which, the previous day, all but one of the servants had fled because they could not longer endure the sounds of his suffering. At the sixth vertebra, Sir William's divining hand evoked a scream that was repeated as he gently pressed at two adjacent points. The diagnosis of spinal tumour was conveyed to the sweating, exhausted patient, who cried out: 'Call the surgeon. Call him at once!'

An implacable foe of the anti-vivisectionists, Horsley had

perfected his technique by operating on monkeys. Even so, no surgeon could think lightly of the difficulties and risks of operating on the human spine: 'and the best surgeons might well dread the possibility of doing it for the first time'.[1] Safeguarded as he was by the thoroughness of his preparations, and by his consummate skill, Horsley showed signs of strain as he made his incision between the third and seventh vertebrae. The tumour he was looking for lay higher up the spinal canal than he had expected, needing an extension of the wound. As he appeared to hesitate, Charles (later Sir Charles) Ballance, his assistant, urged him forward. The almond-shaped tumour was found and beautifully removed.

Six months afterwards, Horsley brought his patient before a meeting of the surgical section of the Medical Society of London. Captain Gilbey confirmed that he had done with crutches and was walking three miles a day, though with some stiffness of the legs. In six months more, he was leading an active life again. Horsley's achievement was saluted by the world's surgeons. He had triumphantly emerged from a contest with fate that no man before had dared to face.

*

Horsley's embroilments with the anti-vivisectionists, women's suffrage, the drink question, Liberal politics, were not the only factors working against his popularity. He was admired and disliked, criticised and envied. His personality contained elements of masterful disdain that offended many. Dr Alfred Cox, for many years medical secretary of the British Medical Association, emphasised from long and close acquaintance that 'the man who could be overbearing and even insolent to his equals and "superiors" was always most considerate to smaller men.'

He made it known that he would retire from practice at sixty and go into Parliament. During the General Election of 1910, he stood as Liberal candidate for London University and was defeated. His house in Cavendish Square was plastered with

[1] Paget.

Sir John Murray, the distinguished London publisher, who championed Dr Axham in letters to *The Times* and other newspapers.

Mrs Axham, 'a most beautiful woman' (Barker). She remained devotedly loyal to her husband during his many years as a medical outcast.

Left : Sir William Arbuthnot Lane, who believed that the colon was the source of many human ills, and who founded the New Health Society. *Below left :* Lord Dawson of Penn, who was at the deathbed of George V and who wrote the memorable bulletin announcing that 'the King's life is moving peacefully to its close'. *Below right :* Sir Harold Gillies. His experiences in the First World War led to the development of a new branch of modern surgery.

posters cartooning his opponents. In 1913, he was invited to stand for Market Harborough. His views on female suffrage were too progressive for his local sponsors, who sent him away unadopted. His attitude to women was always one of deep regard. 'Contempt for women', he would say, 'is the foundation of sex immorality.' He would have it that intellectual capacity invariably comes from the mother.

He sought refuge from the inaction of the first months of the war in the big sky-lighted workshop that he had made for himself out of the former occupant's billiard room at 25 Cavendish Square. Experimenting there with chemical reagents, he stained his fingers apparently indelibly, causing one of his wealthy women patients to say: 'I like Sir Victor, but I do wish he would wash his hands before he comes to see me.'

His condemnation of the rum ration for the troops plunged him into a maelstrom of public controversy, from which he emerged unconverted and unbowed. 'He was in the wrong there: he spoke and wrote in a style unworthy of him. But he was horrified by the evil, in the winter of 1914–15, of the heavy drinking everywhere, the increase of drunkenness among women, the crazy treating, all the steps of the dance on the edge of the precipice—to him it was heartbreaking.'[1]

He was once referred to as the Achilles of his profession. His vulnerability was more diffuse, if less obvious, than that of the classical hero. For weapons, he used tendentious and sometimes offensive remarks. He rebuked the Archbishop of York for speaking charitably of the Kaiser, and chided Viscount Morley for obtuseness in a biographical work. Sir Victor, it seems, was asserting another of his alienating concepts, that all men are equal in the sight of God.

In appearance and style, he was an aristocrat, though his his origins were sturdily middle-class: he was the son of a Royal Academician. He was educated at Cranbrook School in Kent, and at University College, London, His good looks were concentrated in the upper part of his face, set off by a 'flare' of white hair over the forehead. He carried himself like

[1] Paget.

a captain of men. 'When he came into a dull roomful of guests, there was an odd effect as if the lamps went up of their own accord.'[1] His musical laugh was heard often. Speaking, his *th* became *v*. He was one of the first consultants within the Harley Street consortium to instal a telephone, and he renounced the frock coat and silk hat long before most of his medical colleagues.

His written appeals to the Director-General of the Army Medical Service at the War Office in the autumn of 1914 at first went unanswered. 'Is it not possible for me to be given an appointment as surgeon to a Base Hospital either in England or on the Continent?' wrote the man whose experimental and operative work inspired most later developments in brain surgery. 'I will wait on you tomorrow on the chance of your being able to see me. I may say I have my kit and could leave at once.'

Eating his heart out in enforced idleness (his own words) and sardonically reminding himself that 'in the Boer War no one of any independence of thought was selected,' he joined the Union of Democratic Control, founded by Radical MPs and members of the Independent Labour Party, sharing their conviction that war was a disease curable by democracy and universal suffrage. Not until 1915 was he given a post as head of the surgical division of the 21st General Hospital, with the rank of captain, RAMC. It was no tribute to his experience and gifts. In the late spring of that year he departed for Mesopotamia and never came back. Sir James Purves-Stewart wrote that Horsley 'used to maintain the thesis' that teetotallers were immune from sunstroke. His sudden death the following year at Asmara was said to have been due to it. Paratyphoid may have been a truer diagnosis.

*

That was a difficult time, too, for Sir Felix Semon, KCVO, MD, FRCP, the genial, warm-hearted, and courtly German-Jewish laryngologist, of 39 Wimpole Street, who had been

[1] Paget.

prominent in the tragedy of the Emperor Frederick, and who, as a consequence, counted Queen Victoria and King Edward VII among his patients. His habitual bidding, 'Open your mouse, and breeze qvite qvietly,' became a humorous catchphrase in neighbouring consulting-rooms.

Long residence and practice in London, and a loyal attachment to the country of his adoption, did not immunise him from the recriminations of the more frenzied type of patriot when war came. Three of his sons joined the British Army in 1914; even so, their father had to suffer, among other exasperations, frequent visits from the police through the war years. His tennis court at Rignalls, Great Missenden, brought him under suspicion. 'It was alleged that I had secretly constructed it for German howitzers.'

He wrote of the loneliness that gathered about him at that time. 'A few of our acquaintances still invite us or call upon us; but the large majority have become perfectly mute. What a sad decline of a once richly blessed life!' He and his wife had long been familiar figures in the social and artistic life of London. They gave musical evenings at which she sang to his piano accompaniments.

One of his notable patients was Sir John Millais, whose life, Semon considered, 'was needlessly sacrificed, when he might still have produced imperishable works'. The artist was attacked by laryngeal cancer. 'When I first saw him professionally, it was without exception, the most promising case for operation which I have ever seen! There could not be the slightest doubt that if the patient had at that time submitted to thyrotomy, which I most strenuously advised, his life would have been prolonged for a number of years.' Semon's optimism was often suspect among his medical colleagues. His greatest service was in gaining the recognition of laryngology as a specialist's subject.

The Lancet reported that the medical profession had shown itself to be as patriotic in responding to the call-up 'as any other'. Most of the younger men had gone from Harley Street, having made practice sharing arrangements with older colleagues. There were instances of general practitioners moving in from the suburbs to occupy newly vacated consulting-rooms and putting up their plates, implying specialist status. Brass name plates, 'deeply engraved and specially adapted for the profession' were obtained from Cooke & Co., Finsbury Pavement, E.C., price 10s. 6d.

A drugs shortage soon became manifest at home and along the battlefronts. Harley Street was comfortably close to the fount of origin of the new amyl nitris emergency capsules, 'valuable in arresting haemorrhage and shock'. There was more than casual interest in the suggestion made in *Science Progress* that 'a special vitamine' might be pathogenically involved in cancer. *The Lancet* asked whether diet regulation, 'with a view of excluding the vitamine', was feasible.

Gun deafness was a more pressing topic of the day. Jobson Horne, MD, ear, nose and throat specialist, of 11 Wimpole Street, reminded his professional colleagues that naval officers indulged the precautionary habit of 'chewing a toothpick whilst big guns are firing'. Some aural surgeons were recommending the Mallock Ear Defender invented by a Fellow of the Royal Society. It insulated the inner ear from pressure changes.

*

At 133 Harley Street, Sir James Mackenzie, doyen of heart specialists, had been contemplating what to Dr R. Macnair Wilson, his biographer, was 'an amazing project'. Having risen to the professional heights, he proposed to return to general practice in the provinces. One of the thinking physicians, he desired to show that his life's work was a signpost to the future of the well-equipped family doctor.

Mackenzie never forgot that the larger part of his experience was gained as a provincial doctor. He was a Highland farmer's son who entered the profession by way of a chemist's shop in Perth and Edinburgh University. Having qualified, he became assistant to a 'firm' of general practitioners at Bank Parade, Burnley. The death of a young woman patient from heart failure in childbirth affected him deeply. It made him a heart specialist.

With the help of a local watchmaker named Shaw, he devised an instrument which simultaneously recorded the cardiac, venous, and arterial pulses, enabling him to analyse and pronounce upon heart irregularities. The instrument was known as Mackenzie's Ink Polygraph and, says his biographer, it was eventually used 'by all heart specialists in Europe and America'. He declined to capitalise his invention, preferring that it should continue to be manufactured locally and made available to doctors at a fraction above cost. In time, he almost regretted having invented it because it brought him honour that he would rather have earned by diagnostic insight. He objected to the sneering implication of the term 'bedside baronets' applied to certain Harley Street personages, asking: 'Where else should a doctor be?'

His strength and success as a cardiac specialist were founded on the rich experience of his provincial years. Thirty lay behind him when he arrived in Harley Street in 1907, at the age of fifty-four. It was his principal asset, for he had no private means, no connection among medical men who might send him patients, no distinctions. It weighed little in London that he had recently been honoured by an invitation to address the medical school at Leeds University, though the occasion drew a generous reference to his work from Sir Berkeley Moynihan, the North of England's most respected surgeon.

In his first year as a London specialist Mackenzie earned £114 in fees. He had time on his hands to write *Diseases of the Heart*. It led to his being put in charge of the new heart department at London Hospital. His election to the Royal College of Physicians was followed by the Fellowship of the Royal Society, most illustrious of scientific bodies, and a knighthood which surprised him more than it did his colleagues in medicine.

His £100-a-year back room on the ground floor of 133 Harley Street became a place of pilgrimage for patients and doctors from many countries. It contained none of the paraphernalia of success with which lesser men surrounded themselves. Simplicity was the keynote. Affectation could not survive in Mackenzie's presence. His consulting-room was his kingdom and he ruled it. When Lord Northcliffe, the greatest newspaper magnate of the age, went to him in fear of *angina pectoris*, demanding 'a frank opinion', Mackenzie told him: 'This is not a newspaper office.'

Sketching his personality, Dr Macnair Wilson said that 'courage radiated from his eyes, a splendid-looking man, tall, broad-shouldered, with massive brows and the clear, masterful features of physical and mental strength'. An inspiring humility infused his nature. 'He was exquisitely simple, as simple as a child.'

He saw the war as 'really a test at the greatest scale of the adequacy of medical knowledge'. It was found to be seriously wanting, 'for large numbers of perfectly healthy men were rejected because they presented signs whose value the medical examiners were unable to assess'. The war hospitals were full of so-called cases of v.d.h. (valvular disease of the heart) and d.a.h. (disordered action of the heart), when in fact Mackenzie was able to show that eighty per cent were not suffering from any form of heart disease and were capable of the exertions forbidden them by their medical officers. The study of the 'soldier's heart' syndrome was concentrated at Mount Vernon Hospital, Hampstead. As its chief consultant, Sir James Mackenzie helped to give England the leadership of the new cardiology.

V

A NEW BRANCH OF SURGERY

The Barker controversy came before the public again in December 1914. A long article on the case of Dr Axham, written by the Rev. J.L. Walton, of Southend-on-Sea, appeared in that month's issue of the *Nineteenth Century*. Its temperate and convincing recital was followed by the offer of editorial space to 'any responsible surgeon' who wished to challenge the particular assumptions of the article. There was no response. Barker was not surprised. The new policy of his opponents, he decided, was 'mum's the word'.

A patient named Pratt, of The Pharmacy, Station Road, New Barnet, wrote to him on 16 May 1915: 'I am convinced that if I had not seen you I should either have committed suicide or gone mad, as I could not have stood the pain much longer.' On a letter signed J. Lumsden, of Auckland Road, Upper Norwood, testifying to the successful treatment of his son, Barker wrote marginally: 'A Waterhouse blunder!'

During the first eighteen months of the war a long procession of men crippled by training or active service at the front passed through his hands. Many, if not most, had been unsuccessfully treated by the doctors. In some cases, 'benevolent persons' paid the fees. In many, Barker made no charge. The *English Review* for October 1916 gave the history of typical cases, and drew attention to the fact that the War Office had rejected Barker's offer 'to treat gratuitously would-be recruits rejected as unfit owing to some physical disablement that had not yielded to ordinary professional methods'. The Surgeon-General would have none of it. 'Mr Barker is not qualified.'

A renewal of Barker's offer was supported by a memorial signed by a cousin of the King, several admirals and generals, and other well-known public figures. Lord Kitchener's sister, Mrs Frances Parker, wrote to the *Globe* newspaper, giving details of the case of a private soldier named Townley, of the Royal West Kent Regiment, who had been discharged as unfit for further service. 'Two visits to Mr Barker put him right, and thus a man has been saved for the country and so much pension money for the national purse.' Five officers of the 3rd Oxford and Bucks Light Infantry had returned to the front after being treated by Barker. One of them, Major Wheeler, wrote: 'All five of us had been to at least two different medical practitioners. Not one of them was able to give us any relief.'

Vice-Admiral Mark Kerr, 'late Commander-in-Chief of the Greek Navy', testified in the *English Review* to Barker's skill, 'after some months of suffering', and thought it 'nothing short of a crime' that his offer was declined by the War Office. A major-general was stated to have been 'twice operated on by Mr Barker with complete success'.

Among Barker's papers is a list of his Army officer patients of various ranks. It gives 206 names, among them Generals Dobbie, Gough, and Dawnay. The *English Review* protested that 'it will be a scandal beyond words if men have to face the difficult days which will follow the war *crippled*, and to that extent *handicapped*, because when they were under treatment pride, prejudice, ignorance, had their fate in their hands and sacrificed them to satisfy a professional caste'.

Indignant because his wife had suffered needlessly at the hands of 'eminent surgeons' before being treated by Barker, Sir Arthur Markham, MP for Mansfield, asked a question in the House of Commons about War Office obduracy in responding to Barker's offer of his services. The Under-Secretary of State, H. J. Tennent, 'declined to interfere', and wrote a courteous private letter to Barker giving the reason. 'It would open the doors for the admission of many others whom I am sure you would consider to be quite undesirable.'

Barker interpreted the letter as a sign that while the War Office might co-operate, the medical authorities remained firm in their stand against him.

Sixty back benchers took up the case. They formed an Injured Soldiers' Committee to storm the barriers. More questions were asked in the House. Will Thorne, a Labour member who had been cured by Barker of a long-standing injury, told the Commons that 3,000 men had been discharged from the Army 'owing to derangements of knee cartilages'. Another member rose up to say that 'those who are being discharged as incurable are victimised by prejudice'. Barker gained a particularly influential backer when he operated on the Minister of Labour, John Hodge, who weighed seventeen stone and who had displaced a semi-lunar cartilage while stepping down from a hansom cab. The Minister arranged a dinner party for fifty MPs at the House of Commons, with Barker as the guest of honour.

Though only one other person knew it, his devoted wife, Barker was himself a suffering man. 'The gnawing, almost incessant pain in my spine sapped my strength'. He felt 'more and more worn with controversy'. The bitterness of the medical opposition weighed heavily on him. 'It worried and saddened me'.

Holbrook Jackson, the London bookman and essayist, wrote in 1916 that 'in appearance Mr Barker is difficult to place. Of medium height and slight athletic build; crisp and dark of hair which looks as if it would stand on end if permitted, and strong ascetic features, he might pass for a priest or a poet, or better still a musician.' Jackson noted the 'strong nervous play' of Barker's hands, and compared them with the hands of Kubelik, the violinist. He asked Barker whether he could impart his skill to others, and received the answer: 'You can teach anybody to play the violin, but you can't make a Paganini of anybody.' His manner was habitually courteous. Behind the sympathetic smile there was a hardness indicative of the strength of will that carried him through many a nerve-racking operation.

Unexpectedly, in November 1916 the *Medical Press* opened its columns to a full discussion of manipulative surgery—'the very journal which had heaped scorn upon my offending head!' (Barker). Attempts to secure the publication of his letters in the *British Medical Journal* and *The Lancet* 'had failed conspicuously'. Now the *Medical Press* printed two letters from doctors giving personal knowledge of Barker's skill. One of them, Frank Collie, MD, of 14 Balham Park Road, S.W. referred to him as 'a genius'.

Attention was drawn to the doctors' letters in a leading article, in which an important submission was made. 'So far from holding any brief for Mr Barker or his friends, we have not infrequently joined in the orthodox chorus against him on the ground that he is unqualified, but now, in so far as we can secure it, we are quite determined that he and they shall have a fair hearing.'

Dr Leonard Williams, of 123 Harley Street, with Dr Collie, and Dr Arthur Latham, of St George's Hospital, London, called on Barker in Park Lane to discuss what could be done to persuade the medical faculty to agree to his giving a formal demonstration of his methods. Barker wrote after their visit: 'Nothing could have been kinder or more conciliatory than the demeanour of these three men. I could not help smiling as I pondered the change that was coming over the more progressive and charitable members of the profession.'

For the next three months the *Medical Press* published letters from doctors telling their experiences of Barker's cures, and endorsing his claim to recognition. Their statements made it clear that a wide gap remained in orthodox surgical knowledge and teaching, and that much suffering resulted from it. As for Barker's peculiar skill, the editor of *Medical Press* published the summarising comment that 'on this point there can be no manner of doubt. The witnesses who have testified in our columns, among whom are surgeons of the greatest distinction, constitute a weight and volume of evidence which it is quite impossible to cast aside.'

Barker himself seems to have ignored the fact that his

methods had long been practised by qualified surgeons, if not at his level of competence. In 1914, W. B. Maxwell, a well-known novelist, was rejected by the Army because of what he wrote of as 'my great disability', a foot that had been crippled since he was eleven. Its displaced bones were successfully manipulated by M. H. Gardiner, LRCS, a police surgeon, of The Green, Richmond, Surrey—'the beginning of a miracle for me,' Maxwell wrote. Enabled to walk easily again, he was commissioned in the 10th Royal Fusiliers.[1]

*

At the old Army hospital at Aldershot named after the Duke of Cambridge, a young New Zealand surgeon of Scottish descent, who had signed on 'for the duration', was performing a series of often desperately urgent operations that became the inspiration of an entirely new branch of surgical practice and took him finally to Harley Street—'to the snob value of which', he subsequently wrote, 'few of us are immune'. The young surgeon's name was Gillies.

A captain in the Royal Army Medical Corps, he was not disposed to take himself seriously on that account. Place and rank at no time much impressed him. Pomposity amused and irritated him. His freakish sense of humour, akin to that of his collateral forebear, Edward Lear, was always near the surface, an unpredictable streak in his nature that was often an embarrassment to his colleagues and was to become more so in the years ahead. It was allied to an unshakable nerve that was tested by some of the most ghastly mutilations ever seen in war or peace.

Having helped to row Cambridge to victory in the Boat Race of 1904, Harold Delf Gillies received his medical education at St Bartholomew's Hospital, London, studying ear, nose and throat surgery under Sir Milsom Rees (1866–1952), laryngologist to Their Majesties. He became Sir Milsom's assistant at 18 Upper Wimpole Street, a £10 a week appoint-

[1] *Time Gathered* (1937).

ment that he believed was given to him for his prowess as a golfer rather than for his surgical ability. He attended his chief at the operation on the Prince of Wales [later Edward VIII] for adenoids at Buckingham Palace in 1912. He also deputised for Sir Milsom as medical adviser to the singers of the Royal Opera House, Covent Garden, spraying their throats and giving them injections. He incurred the displeasure of Madame Melba by letting golf take precedence over one of his appointments with her. It was the year in which he won the most coveted trophy in amateur golf, the Royal St George's Grand Challenge Cup. The first-class golfer was also a gifted player of other games, and an accomplished musician and painter in oils.

Serving with the British Red Cross in France early in 1915, he saw that in trench warfare the head and face were more vulnerable than any other part of the soldier's body, requiring new surgical applications. Harassed general surgeons at the base hospital were treating facial wounds by drawing the severed tissues together, stitching them up, and trusting to nature to do the rest. Nature could not be relied on to replace all lost tissue and bone, especially where the cellular destruction was severe. Men were often sent back to their units with permanently distorted features, depressing the morale of their fellows. Gillies soon learnt that every soldier dreaded facial wounds.

At the Aldershot hospital in 1916 he was fortunate in having the goodwill of Arbuthnot Lane, medical head of the command. Lane ensured that Gillies had the two hundred extra beds he needed as the battlefield casualties mounted that summer. Sister Catherine Black, of London Hospital, was on duty at Aldershot during Gillies' time there. She had served at casualty clearing stations at the front. What she saw at Aldershot, she wrote, surpassed in horror the worst of her experiences in France. She nursed 'men with half their faces literally blown to pieces, with the skin left hanging in shreds and the jawbones crushed to a pulp that felt like sand under your fingers'. She recalled Gillies' concern for his patients, the tender care he showed. 'Don't worry, sonny,' he would say. 'You'll be all right. You'll have as good a face as most of us before we've finished with you.'

His extraordinary achievement in keeping that routine promise to so high a proportion of his war patients, plus his success in 'badgering the authorities', resulted in the establishment of the Queen's Hospital at Sidcup, Kent. There modern plastic surgery came into its own. It was there that, in a flash of intuition in the operating theatre, he devised the 'tube pedicle', a new and quite revolutionary method of skin grafting that brightened the prospects of disfigured persons everywhere.

Gillies brought his artistic temperament to bear on every phase of his innovating work, and by doing so added force to the declaration of his contemporary, Sir Heneage Ogilvie, MD, FRCS, that 'it can be claimed, and not without reason, that every surgical advance of major importance has come from this country'. The skill with which Gillies renewed shattered faces showed sculptural affinities that entitled his branch of surgery to be more nearly regarded an art than any other. Perfecting his techniques from the fumbling 'flap' closure of face wounds in the First World War, he broadened the possibilities of plastic surgery to bring new hope to sufferers from hereditary deformities that made life miserable for so many. That he also devised operations of a more frivolous kind, ministering to human vanity, cannot detract from the grandeur of his finest achievements. As well as a great surgeon, he was a pre-eminent teacher who, in the words of his admiring friend and physician, Lord Evans, 'produced from some of his pupils a greatness not far short of his own'. Reviewing the biography of him, *Gillies, Surgeon Extraordinary*, published in 1964, *The Times* said that 'he was a great, good, ebullient, and unforgettable man'.

*

'I shall have to ask the indulgence of the House . . .' The member for Devizes, Basil (later Sir Basil) Peto, rose on 14 August 1917 to speak 'on a matter which has been one of

rather acute controversy,' namely, the offer made by Herbert
Barker of free treatment for men of the Services invalided from
the battle fronts by reason of injuries curable by manipulative
surgery, and its rejection by the authorities. The member's
speech filled seven pages of Hansard. It included a quotation
from a written statement by the Minister of Labour giving his
personal experience of Barker's remedial skill.

'The Army Council are clamouring for men, but won't,
owing to the conservative stupidity of the doctors, remove the
ban upon Mr Barker, who could very quickly give back hundreds of these men to service once again. Oh, the stupidity
and cruelty of it! Why can't the Medical Trade Union remove
their restrictions for the period of the war just as the work-
men's trade unions have done?'

The voice of Harley Street was heard when Sir Watson
Cheyne, who had taken his seat the previous day as the new
member for the Scottish Universities, intervened in the debate
to say that he was 'rather in a fog as to what proposition has
to be met in regard to this gentleman', meaning Barker. 'I do
not know what it is he wants us to do. If he wants to join a
massage corps, I do not suppose anybody will object. He
simply joins the medical service and becomes an orderly and
carries out the instructions which he gets.'

Sir Watson then gave his views on bonesetting. 'The human
form is a very delicate organization. It is not a thing which
should be meddled with by people who do not know it as
intimately as it is possible to know it.' He threw in the admission that Barker was doing 'very good work'. His patronising
air brought a rebuke from a famous journalist of the day,
James Douglas, writing in *London Opinion*: 'Seeing that Mr
Barker in his unorthodox surgery is as eminent as Sir Watson
Cheyne in his orthodox surgery, his remarks strike me as being
the last word in discourtesy.'

In the *Nineteenth Century* for October 1917, Barker replied
to Watson Cheyne with a number of extracts from letters
written to him by qualified medical men, and recited particulars of some of his latest successes. 'Sir Watson hinted at the

tragedies which *may* happen through a visit to a bonesetter. Has he ever thought of the tragedies that *have* occurred through patients *not* visiting a bonesetter? Is it not a tragedy that people should be left lame, in pain, enduring inconvenience for years, going from one famous surgeon to another without relief, when relief can be afforded, often in a few minutes, by manipulative operations? I come across such cases literally every hour of my working life.'

Noting that Watson Cheyne agreed that he was 'doing very good work', Barker demanded 'to be treated with decency by the Faculty and not as though I were a pretentious charlatan'. Among the medical men who had gone to him for treatment not procurable from their fellows were Dr Sutherland Rees-Phillips, Dr Montague Lomax, Dr Martin Flack, and Dr C. Wheeler. Flack was Demonstrator of Physiology at London Hospital. His knee trouble had resisted relief at the hands of his qualified colleagues for fifteen years. Barker put it right in as many days. Dr Wheeler, another sufferer from persistent knee trouble, had been seen by three orthopaedic surgeons, one of them 'the most famous practitioner in England', presumably, Sir Robert Jones, FRCS, of Liverpool and Cavendish Square. He was also treated in hospital, without result. Reviewing the case, Barker wrote: 'It was not without some appreciation of the irony of the position that I manipulated that knee into its normal condition, and sent the doctor away— amazed and very grateful.'

A. E. Cumberbatch, FRCS, 11 Park Crescent, W., sent Barker a patient who had not found help elsewhere, prompting Barker to reflect in writing: 'This, then, is the position. While the profession dubs me an impudent pretender in public, leaders of it send me their failures in private.' Cumberbatch wrote enthusiastically about the good result of his recommendation. A few months later, he himself arrived unexpectedly at Barker's consulting-room. 'He saw the surprise on my face and smiled as he said: "Yes, Barker, you guess right. I've come to consult you. You're entitled to smile".' He was suffering from a spinal injury.

Having remedied the condition and received Cumberbatch's 'warm thanks and praise', Barker asked him whether
he would 'write a paper, setting forth the truth of this matter'.
The surgeon preferred not to commit himself beyond verbal
appreciation. To Barker, 'it was a bitter disappointment'.

Watching him at work, those medical patients of his may
have felt, as many laymen did, that he had at his command a
subtle power that was beyond definition. He was often heard to
say after completing certain operations: 'I don't know how I
did it.' In cases with a history of low back pain he had a knack
of numbing the nerve centres without recourse to anaesthetics. When he had occasion to use force, he sometimes
appeared to exert it less by muscular effort than by an hypnotic
influence imposed not on the patient but on himself. His set,
intense facial expression as he worked, his flashing hands, his
air of transcendent self-assurance, produced an effect of
wizardry that made many of his patients feel that they were in
the presence of an exceptional being.

*

If the debate in the House of Commons failed of its purpose,
which was to secure acceptance of Barker's offer of free treat-
men for men of the Services, the importance of the arena in
which it was staged gave wide publicity to the cause of manipulative surgery, and to the obscurantist attitudes of medical
orthodoxy. A minor concession was won. The Under-
Secretary of State for War agreed 'that there was no objection
to a soldier going, if he wishes, to have treatment from an
unqualified man, on his own responsibility'. The Army
Council promptly issued an instruction that the Government
would not be responsible for 'untoward results' arising from
such cases. *The Globe* considered that the debate was 'a signal
triumph for the medical trade union'.

George Bernard Shaw urged that 'the sensible way out of
the difficulty would be to give Mr Barker an honorary degree,
just as Oxford makes Mr Lloyd Geroge a Doctor of Civil Law.
The General Medical Council is less liberal because it is, first,

88 Harley Street, where multiple letting and the resultant proliferation of doctors' name-plates first began, in the early 1920s.

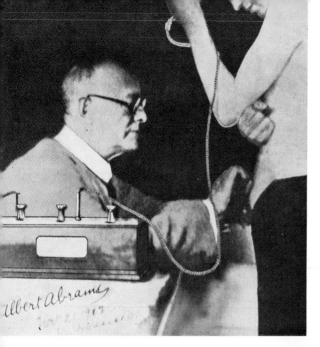

Left : The Abrams Box, 'adopted in good faith by a few experimentally-minded practitioners in Harley Street, exploited like a fruit machine for its profitability by others'. *Below :* Harley Street in the 1920s, before the days of parking meters and traffic wardens.

last, and all the time, a trade union. Therefore, you have this silly scandal of a surgical manipulator of genius forbidden to treat our disabled soldiers simply because the profession is too preoccupied with its own privileges.' Every surgeon, Shaw suggested, should be a bonesetter, 'especially in the country, where accidents are common and there are no specialists at hand'.[1]

Sir Archibald Macdonald, Bart., told *The Nation* that he had been cured of 'helpless lameness' by Barker, and that on one of his visits he spoke to three Army officers in the waiting-room. 'Each of them was about to be placed on half-pay owing to injuries received on active service. I saw each of these officers walk out of Mr Barker's consulting-room perfectly sound and with several types of knee-caps they had been wearing protruding from their pockets.'

Barker's practice had grown 'to unimaginable proportions' (his phrase). He was seeing as many as thirty patients a day, sometimes more. The telephone rang incessantly. Appointments often had to be made weeks in advance. Every post brought letters begging for his help. His spine was still a source of personal distress. 'I was beginning to feel the wear and tear of my work. It was made more burdensome by the long and unequal fight with the Faculty.' It does not appear that he sought the help of the osteopaths who were reputedly competent to deal with spinal disorders.

Often, after a day's work, 'I had scarcely the energy to walk from Park Lane to Marble Arch', on his way home to Hampstead. He believed that 'even a strong man would have felt the strain of what I undertook, day after day, year after year'. He compared his kind of work with that of the orthodox surgeon, acknowledging the mental sensitivity required by the latter, and the possibility of exhaustion resulting from it. 'But the physical expenditure of energy is small. With the manipulative surgeon it is different. Many manipulative operations call for a great deal of muscular effort. To this is added just as great a strain as the cutting surgeon has to stand up to.'

[1] *English Review*, January 1918.

H. G. Wells was the latest in the lengthening list of his distinguished patients. 'He had been lame for months, the usual type of case so commonly neglected by the medical profession when a few minutes ought to have sufficed to put it right.' Augustus John offered to 'do a head' of him. 'If you will rattle my bones, I should be more than repaid!'[1] He and John had been friends since 1913. The artist had sought him out in a remote holiday village in Devon, begging him to relieve him of the misery of 'an obstinately troublesome knee'. He had brought 'immense relief' to Lady Samuel, wife of the High Commissioner for Palestine. Sir Edward Marshall Hall, the famous advocate, had foot trouble. 'I want to ask you to look at it.' He had interested himself in Dr Axham's case, and urged Barker to persuade Axham to take action against the General Medical Council, promising: 'He can count on my services without fee or reward.'

[1] Augustus John's portrait of Barker was exhibited at the Grafton Galleries in 1921.

VI

END OF THE SILK HAT ERA

In 1918, Sir Bertrand Dawson, who, between his duties as a temporary major-general of the Royal Army Medical Corps, was seeing patients at 32 Wimpole Street, stood out as an advocate of medicine at the service of the community rather than as the perquisite of individuals who could pay for it. His Cavendish Lecture, delivered to the West London Medico-Chirurgical Society on the future of the profession, included an appeal for 'medical team work' that can be seen now as inspirational in its long-term view. The absence of medical representation from the governing circle, noted many years before by Sir Morell Mackenzie, would soon be repaired. A medical statesman was in the making.

Dawson had been prominent among the doctors of his day from the time that King Edward VII died, in 1910. His name was on the lips of many more people five years later when King George V was thrown from his horse, during a visit to the Western Front, and so seriously hurt that the truth could not then be told. The bulletins were signed by Sir Frederick Treves and Dawson; professionally, it was obvious that Dawson was in charge of the case. Soon the Court Circular was referring to him as Physician-in-Ordinary to His Majesty 'in the room of Sir Francis Laking, deceased'. In France, he had been looking after the health of the British Ambassador, Lord Bertie, and he attended Lloyd George, the Prime Minister, on his latest visit to General Headquarters. Dawson's was the brightest ascending star in British medicine.

He was one of the seven children of a Croydon architect, who sent him to St Paul's School for two years, after which he was entered as a student at what Arnold of Rugby referred to as 'that godless institution in Gower Street', University College, London. He took his BSC. there, a distinction which gave him more private satisfaction than any of the medical degrees that came later. At University College he knew what it was to live at a meagre subsistence level. His biographer says that 'he was often down to three-and-sixpence before sending home the signal of distress'.[1]

The experience gave an edge to his social awareness. While not apparently seeking political affinities, he shared some of the progressive views of the period. As a medical student, he spoke at Hyde Park Corner on birth control, then regarded as a daring topic for public discussion.

He and a contemporary walked up Gower Street late one night. Dawson asked his companion: 'How much have you got?' They could not muster the bus fare that would have averted a midnight trudge to Holloway, N., where they had lodgings. The two did not meet again for over forty years: then their venue was Buckingham Palace. Dawson's companion of that night's walk long before was Ramsay MacDonald, who had become Prime Minister. Recalling it, MacDonald told the Royal Society of Medicine in 1929 that Dawson's 'striking distinction' stood out in the throng at the Palace, 'as if he was born there'.

A fine appearance was not the least of his personal assets, the more so as his grace of manner ensured that others were not made too uncomfortably aware of their lack of it. His personality was as attractive to kings as to commoners. The Dean of Lichfield thought him 'almost too handsome, too *soigné*, too much a man of the world, but after five minutes this assessment had to be revised'. He was notably successful with persons of attainment who bore burdens of responsibility through the crises of middle age. A foremost authority on hypertension, he was understood to have originated the familiar twentieth-century definition, 'diseases of stress'.

It was said of Dawson that he had more wisdom than know-

[1] *Dawson of Penn*, by Francis Watson (Chatto & Windus, 1950).

ledge. His second opinion on a medical colleague who had been bedridden five months, in the care of thirteen other doctors, had the patient up and about in three days. He liked to have what he called 'the full picture', to find out all he could about a patient's way of life, more than was to be divined by routine clinical procedures. It had the effect of a prelude to analytical reasoning, which in Dawson's case it may not have been. The present writer made diary notes of a consultation with him in Wimpole Street between the wars:

'A wealthy patient preceded me, the head of one of the largest London departmental stores. I had interviewed him once, and when our eyes met as I entered Lord Dawson's waiting-room, he quickly averted his as if he were chagrined at being caught in that place after all the pompous talk he had given out about success and the tremendous satisfactions that go with it. He was with Dawson for no more than ten minutes and left with uncertain steps, as a man might who had received no remission of sentence.

'I expected to be disposed of stethoscopically equally soon. It was not so. Perhaps Lord Dawson, so vibrantly alive himself, saves time on those who have had their chance and abused it in order to spend a little more over those who are young enough to benefit by his counsel. To him health is unmistakably the greatest of human prerogatives. He carried out his examination of me so quickly and deftly that he might have been measuring me for a new suit instead of for a more sensible style of living. And then he stood in front of his fireplace, his hands joined under his morning coat tails, and gave me fifty minutes' good talking to.

'What he said was a distillation of pure common sense. He used no fashionable jargon. He suggested no short cuts. He signposted the road to health afresh for me, so that I knew that if I got lost again the fault would be mine, and not necessarily attributable to the economic drive or even civilisation, which we so conveniently blame for most modern ills.

'He has been lucky in his physical endowment. Nature gave him quiet but impressive strength. From his eyes shines a sanity that must of itself have been the solvent of many of his patients' complexes. When he looks at you your funny little fads and phobias and obsessions scatter like so many dead leaves. It wasn't at all that I was overwhelmed by his place in the medical hierarchy; his aura is one of kindliness and tolerance and patience. Rather it was that his presence has some magical effect of renewing one's self-confidence, as if one drew subconsciously from his store of wisdom.'

Some of Dawson's contemporaries, who had no reason for jealousy, were cautious in assigning him a place among the great doctors. They considered that his rise to eminence owed more to the impalpable thing called presence than to exceptional ability. He was not a man of intellectual depth. His unpunctuality was as notorious as his patience was admirable. And, as a further sign that he was not immune from ordinary human weakness, he would not allow his age to be quoted in the reference books.

*

In the summer of 1918, Sir Thomas Horder was preoccupied by the case of the Minister of Food, Lord Rhondda, who, two months before taking office the previous year, had been seized by angina pectoris. Raised unexpectedly to ministerial rank, Rhondda predicted that the burden of work and responsibility would accentuate his heart trouble and be the death of him. He was a cheerful hypochondriac who, before the war, had gone from doctor to doctor for heart checks and reassurance of his life expectancy. His sense of the precariousness of human existence may have been sharpened by his experience as a passenger in the *Lusitania*, when that great liner was torpedoed off the Irish coast in 1915 with the loss of a thousand lives. Rhondda, then D. A. Thomas, MP, was rescued after several hours' exposure in a small overcrowded boat.

At the Reform Club, strange stories were told about aspects of his career. The son of a prosperous Welsh grocer, he aspired to political honours as a Senior Wrangler at Cambridge and was soon elected to the House of Commons as a Liberal. He sat for twenty-three years without making any mark. He was a poor speaker who chose to believe that it was a lesser hindrance to his prospects than the hostility of Lloyd George. That audacious fellow-countryman of his wrote some un-flattering verses about him, subsequently published, it was said, in a Welsh-language anthology. Rhondda's lack of con-versation gained him the reputation of a strong silent man.

Married to a woman of higher social class, 'he had no comfort there', as one of his Reform Club friends put it. To that same business associate Rhondda handed bonds worth £25,000, to be made over, in the event of his death, to a woman who was his secret companion installed at St James's Court, S.W. Lord Beaverbrook, who also was a patient of Horder's at that time, knew her. She committed suicide by leaping over a cliff.

Renown was a ruling passion of Rhondda's life: 'the great thing is to be renowned,' he would say. He cultivated his standing with the press. As Food Minister, he was on the whole more popular in Fleet Street than with the public, to whom he remained something of a Celtic mystery figure.

Becoming Minister of Food, he carried a small portable set of scales and weights with him, ostentatiously weighing his meals in restaurants and at banquets to ensure that he was involved in no infringement of his own rationing regulations. Sir Alfred Fripp said of him that as Food Controller 'he car-ried control in his own person too far', and probably hastened his death 'by the way he cut off nourishment unnecessarily'.

Sooner than most politicians of the period, Rhondda saw the need for a Ministry of Health. He advocated it as priority business in the schemes of postwar reconstruction discussed in 1917-18. He dined one night during an air raid with Fripp to meet Sir Cooper Perry, the vastly experienced administrator of Guy's Hospital. They discussed ways of co-ordinating the public health services in a ministry. Fripp afterwards recalled: 'I turned out a particularly good bottle of champagne, which Perry and I enjoyed but which Rhondda, who had violently turned teetotaller, would not touch. He was a man of extremes.' Fripp had been one of his many doctors.

Horder, who attended Rhondda daily, and latterly several times a day, noted that his patient's relish of publicity remained to the end. Special messengers brought batches of press notices about his illness up to his last hours.

Horder found that a Welsh charm against sickness had been secreted under Rhondda's pillow. Once, during Horder's absence, a Welsh 'witch' was called to the dying Minister. Horder was left £10,000 in Rhondda's will, and lost the battle with the Inland Revenue authorities that followed.

*

After the devastating casualty lists of the First World War there came the influenza scourge, which carried off a number of medical men among its million victims, including Dr G. E. Keith, of Manchester Square, W., who in 1894 accompanied Lord Randolph Churchill on his world journey in search of health. *The Lancet* recorded the death, in one week, of three valued medical contributors. The clinical scene was closely akin to that of the last visitation of the kind, in 1892, with the difference that in the earlier epidemic many persons of mature years and distinguished accomplishment were the victims. In 1918, the most vulnerable were seemingly fit young men.

A *Lancet* correspondent described two typical cases. 'One man on being asked how long he had been ill replied: "I was knocked endways this morning at two a.m., suddenly." The other said: "I hadn't been out of bed five minutes when I collapsed." The tone in which they replied conveyed quite clearly to my mind that they were more than considerably disgusted and surprised at the ruthless onset of their troubles. Before the day had closed, they were both expectorating bright red sputum, with a sequel of albuminaria and prolonged delirium.'

Temperatures soared to 104°, the victims often presenting the appearance of crisis. There was hardly a part of the king-

Lionel Logue, C.V.O., of 146 Harley Street, speech therapist to King George VI, photographed with his wife and their three sons before a Buckingham Palace garden party.

The Coronation of George VI. During the ceremony, the King was seen more than once to glance towards his speech therapist, who was given a special place in the Abbey.

Harley Street in the 1950s.

dom that remained immune. Public services were depleted, some paralysed. No earlier outbreak of which there were records exceeded that of 1918 in ferocity and extent. 'The epidemic of 1918–19 led to more deaths than could ever be known.'[1]

For the medical press, it was the prime topic, discussed in leading articles, specially contributed papers, reprinted lectures. His place in the history of medicine not yet assured, the Hunterian Professor, Royal College of Surgeons of England, Alexander Fleming, serving with the research unit attached to a base hospital in France, submitted to *The Lancet* details of his study of the culture media 'for B. influenzae'. His paper did not indicate originality or foreshadow fame.

Harley Street experimented with vaccines, and prescribed permanganate of potash in saline solution; apomorphine in syrup of Virginian prunes; intramuscular injections of mercuric chloride; iodine inhalations; castor oil or calomel purging in conjunction with four-hourly doses of bicarbonate of soda; friar's balsam; and trimethenalallyl-carbide, identified in quotes as 'yadil', the name later given to a patent medicine that was alleged to cure cancer.[2]

Declaring his disbelief in drugs as an influenza specific, Sir Thomas Horder sent his patients to bed in the largest available room, with curtains drawn, windows wide open, superfluous furniture removed, and prescribed a diet of hot fluids, excluding meat extracts and turtle soup. Where there were pulmonary complications, 'brandy or whisky is indicated in small and periodic doses', advice that would have been commended by the Professor of Materia Medica and Therapeutics at Manchester University, who had lately stated 'that it would be of advantage to the community if all distilled spirits were looked upon and used as drugs only'.

[1] Dr Sidney Phillips, at the Harveian Society, 27 April 1922.

[2] The subject of a large-scale advertising campaign, the extravagant claims made for 'Yadil' were exposed by leading medical men, in conjunction with the *Dail Mail*, in 1924.

*

Medicine had lost many of its men of promise in the war. Their obituary photographs in the professional journals showed numbers of them wearing the ribbons of valour. The Royal College of Surgeons mourned twenty-two of its Fellows and Members. At home, there were doctors in uniform, posted to war hospitals and administrative departments, who managed to run practices while drawing Government pay.

The note of grievance was sounded when Sir Watson Cheyne, MP proposed an emergency fund to help doctors whose practices had suffered by their war service. Angry letters were published. An RAMC temporary major declaimed against 'medical men whose practices have been filched from them owing to their absence at the front. These men have been as much injured by their professional brethren as their Belgian colleagues have been by the Hun.' Dr F. R. Mallet retorted in print: 'This is nice sort of language to use of the medical men who have overworked themselves in looking after the patients of absentee doctors as well as their own.'

The doctors sought representation in more than thirty constituencies at the general election of December 1918, and were successful in over a third of them. Dr Christopher Addison (Shoreditch) became the first Minister of Health, Sir Auckland Geddes, MD (Basingstoke) was a future ambassador at Washington.

The publication by the Clarendon Press of *Epidemics Resulting from Wars*, sponsored by the Carnegie Endowment for International Peace, recalled the far-ranging occurrence of syphilis after Charles VIII's expedition to Naples in 1495. Other outbreaks of the same kind were cited as the aftermath of war in Europe. There were ample historical warnings of a menace that might assume greater proportions than ever as the unprecedented demobilisation proceeded in 1919.

Sober citizens were startled when it was announced from the National Council for Combating Venereal Disease at 143 Harley Street that probably 300,000 men of the Services were receiving treatment for infective venereal disease. The inference could only be that the number of infected persons of both sexes much exceeded that figure. Syphilitic mortality was higher than it had been since 1895.

Some doctors had what *The Lancet* referred to as 'a half-expressed dislike' of treating venereal patients and were only too glad to pass such cases on to the new treatment centres that were being set up: 141 in England and Wales, 12 in Scotland, 1 in Ireland. There was a vast secret traffic in dubious ointments, douches, and back street quacks. Those who could afford the fees had the choice of more Harley Street venerologists than had ever practised there before. One of the most successful had a series of cubicles put up to give his patients the privacy denied them in the usual waiting-room. The story is still told of 'a colonel waiting in one cubicle, his wife who had given him v.d. in another, and the subaltern she caught it from in another'. Some of the cases were sent to the specialist in this instance by a hospital porter, who received a commission on successful introductions.

Sir D'Arcy Power, President of the Royal College of Surgeons, warned general practitioners that, 'as an aftermath of the war', they would very likely find 'the sins of the fathers' constituting a hidden source of malaise in the lives of many more patients than before, even in agricultural districts where syphilis was so rare as to be virtually non-existent. He believed that 'the spirochaetal factor' would be found to account for many obscure and remote ailments that were resistant to normal treatment.

A general practitioner sent one of his patients, described as 'an important church dignitary', to see Sir James Purves-Stewart about symptoms of paralysis affecting his palate. Having examined the patient, Sir James telephoned the doctor to ask if there was a possibility that the source of the trouble was syphilitic. The doctor retorted that he would not dream of asking such a question. Sir James therefore took it on himself to do so. 'His Lordship replied: "Yes, I remember having some complaint of the kind when I was an undergraduate".'

Certain professional customs survived the turmoil of 1914–1918. Fellows of the Royal College of Physicians continued to observe their rule of never sending bills. They were paid at the end of consultations or visits in notes or cash enclosed in an envelope or a folded sheet of notepaper. They also maintained their old prerogative of attesting prescriptions with their initials only, plus the date. General practitioners were expected, as before, to sign with their full names.

The war banished the silk hat as a sartorial 'must' in Harley Street, though the older men were not inclined to discard it. A motor car was advertised for sale in the early 1920s as 'specially built to suit the wearer of a top hat in comfort and therefore admirably adapted to the needs of a Harley Street specialist'. Perhaps it was not inherently illogical, if surprising, that some consultants were reluctant to shed what Hazlitt called 'the loathsome finery of the profession of blood'. Sir James Purves-Stewart, who served at Gallipoli and Salonika, noted that colleagues of his on a hospital board 'remained in uniform for months after the war was over'.

VII

HARD TIMES AND CHANGING WAYS

102 Harley Street,
Cavendish Square, W.
27.2.19.

W. Rowley Bristow, FRCS, to Herbert Barker:

Dear Sir—You are operating next Friday on a patient of mine, Mr Savory. If you have no objection, I should like to be present and to watch your manipulations, as I am much interested.

I am,
Yours very truly,
W. ROWLEY BRISTOW

Bristow was the chief orthopaedic surgeon at St Thomas's Hospital, London, and author of *Treatment of Muscle and Joint Injuries*. For a reason not obvious now, Barker declined to allow him to attend, as he asked. He may have felt that Bristow was activated by curiosity rather than by goodwill.

There were signs of dissolving prejudice. Haldin Davis, FRCS, of 17 Cavendish Place, W., sent Barker a test case, and afterwards wrote to *The Lancet* suggesting that it was 'consonant with the dignity of the Royal College of Surgeons of England' to appoint a small committee to look into manipulative surgery. He thought it deplorable 'that we should fail to do our best to make such methods available to the whole of suffering humanity' (10 January 1920).

Three hundred and seven past and present members of

Parliament addressed a petition to the Archbishop of Canterbury, praying that he would confer the Lambeth degree of MD (*honoris causa*) 'upon Mr A. H. Barker, the well-known manipulative surgeon of Park Lane'. Among the signatories were the then Lord Chancellor (Birkenhead), an ex-Home Secretary (Cave), the Attorney-General (Hewart), the Solicitor-General (Pollock), 4 Cabinet Ministers, 2 Lords of the Treasury, 13 Privy Councillors, 11 King's Counsel, 2 Admirals, 4 Generals, 18 Colonels, 19 Majors, 61 Baronets and Knights, and the most prominent members of the Labour Party.

The archbishop was asked to exercise the general right vested in him by the Act of 1534 (25 Henry VIII, c.21, forbidding Papal Dispensations and the payment of Peter's Pence), by which he was given the power to grant 'all manner of such Licences, Dispensations, Compositions, Faculties, Grants, Rescripts, Delegacies, Instruments and all other Writings . . . as heretofore has been used and accustomed to be had and obtained . . . at the See of Rome'. These faculties included degrees. The degree most commonly given by the archbishop was a Doctorate of Divinity. Occasionally, degrees in Music and Civil Law were conferred under the same auspices. The degree of Master of Arts was also given by examination. It was discontinued by Archbishop Davidson after the First World War, on the ground that its validity was diminished by 'the growth of modern universities'.

In the nineteenth century, archbishops of Canterbury had granted Lambeth medical degrees to thirty-one appellants. The Medical Act of 1858 deprived the recipients of the right to practise as medical men. In the case of Barker, Archbishop Davidson consulted legal and medical advisers, among the last-named Sir Rickman Godlee, KCVO, MD, FRCS (1849–1925), Emeritus Professor of Clinical Surgery, University College; Sir Thomas Barlow, FRS, MD (1845–1945), Physician Extraordinary to the King; and Sir Alfred Pearce Gould, KCVO, MS (1852–1922), Consulting Surgeon, Middlesex Hospital. They did not fully endorse the views of the General Medical

Council, and after talking with them the archbishop wrote to Sir Lewis Dibdin, one of the Ecclesiastical Commissioners: 'I feel bound to have a fling at the medical men, who have, as it seems to me, acted in a rather intolerable way towards a man of genius who has got a knack denied to them' (27 May 1920).

The difficulty for the archbishop, and he defined it with judicial care, was that those who signed the petition apparently assumed that the bestowal of a Lambeth medical degree conferred the right to practise medicine. 'This impression', he pointed out, 'is a mistaken one. The legislation which limits registration to men qualified by the ordinary professional training expressly, and I think rightly, provides that the status acquired by registration is not given by the Degree which the petitioners invite me to confer on Mr Barker.' The archbishop thought that people would tend to draw a false premise from the attachment of the title of Doctor to Barker's name. 'On these grounds I come to the conclusion that I should not be acting in the public interest were I to accede to the prayer of the Petition.' His Grace hoped that some other means might be found of marking Barker's 'eminent service to sufferers' (21 June 1920).

The *English Review* considered that 'it does not need much imagination to read between these lines the Primate's private opinion that Mr Barker should be the recipient of some substantial mark of the country's appreciation'. Barker wrote gratefully to the archbishop. He was none the less disappointed in the outcome of the petition, the closing passages of which referred to 'the opposition, contumely, and persecution' that he had faced for so long.

To the Editor, *Manchester City News:*

Sir,—I am a grateful patient of Mr H. A. Barker's (he saved me from lameness in both legs). This controversy has now been proceeding for years—facts on one side, prejudice and vested interests on the other.

One hardly knows at which to marvel most—the universal testimony to Mr Barker's success, unbroken by a single failure, or the ability with which organised medicine maintains its impermeability to a triumphant new idea.

In the end, as ever, truth will prevail.

19 Bouverie Street, E.C.4.   ERNEST PARKE[1]
21 August 1921

For thirty years Barker had fought his battle. Victory was brought nearer by a letter sent to Lloyd George on 6 December 1921 by four medical leaders, Sir Henry Morris, Sir Alfred Fripp, Sir William Arbuthnot Lane, and Sir Bruce Bruce-Porter. They drew the Prime Minister's attention to the hope expressed by the Archbishop of Canterbury that a way might be found of marking public gratitude for Barker's services. 'May we, Sir, express our sympathy with it, and our approval of the efforts which we hear are being made to bring about its fulfilment?'

Perhaps by design, the letter reinforced *sub rosa* activities on Barker's behalf, with politicians and journalists making their own private representations to Downing Street. His name appeared among those of the new knights in the Birthday Honours List of June 1922 with the terse if sufficient citation: 'For services to manipulative surgery.' George Bernard Shaw wrote to Barker years after about his 'dramatically conferred title straight from the throne in the teeth of the GMC.'[2]

Public approval was rarely more sincere or more widely expressed. Bearing the marks of Lloyd George's dubious patronage, the Honours List that year was a contentious one. The *Fortnightly Review*, under its distinguished editor, W. L. Courtney, one of Barker's patients, observed that while 'certain names' in the List 'opened a controversy not soon to be ended', the appearance in it of Barker's name closed a controversy that had lasted many years. 'The Birthday Honours List for 1922 will always stand out as of exceptional interest ... for the universal applause which greeted the appearance

[1] A well-known Fleet Street editor.   [2] In a letter, 12 September 1945.

of one name—that of H. A. Barker.' His smile at the congratulatory deluge broke into quiet shoulder-heaving laughter when
his charwoman, who had been with him for many years,
gazed at him with astonishment on hearing the news and
exclaimed, as if in reproach: 'Oh, Sir '*Er*bert!'

A Fellow of the Royal College of Surgeons, C. O. Haw-
thorne, 63 Harley Street, suggested in print that as leading
members of the profession had been instrumental in securing
the honour for Barker,[1] 'not less strenuous efforts' should be
directed to the position of Dr Axham, 'but for whose co-
operation Mr Barker's activities would either have been
restricted, or, alternatively, would have cost much suffering to
many patients'. The profession could hardly defend a position
in which one was 'promoted to honour' by medical efforts
while the other, by medical verdict, was pronounced guilty of
infamous conduct. 'That one should be exalted and the other
condemned stands open to obvious reproach' (4 June 1922).

W. H. Clayton Greene, FRCS, of 9 Wimpole Street, wrote
to the *British Medical Journal* deploring his colleagues' unwillingness to face squarely the question: Does the manipulative
surgeon possess some special skill by which the public and the
profession should benefit? Giving reasons for not publishing
the letter, the editor, Sir Dawson Williams, MD, stated that
'while it is true that many members of the profession do not
succeed in cases which Barker cures or relieves, they attribute
this to the defective teaching in the medical schools, which
they look upon as inadequate and antiquated' (22 June 1922).
One of Harley Street's thirty women doctors, Octavia Lewin,
MB, wrote to assure Barker that 'nothing short of complete
recognition of you as a full member of the Healing Faculty
could have possibly satisfied us' (June 1922).

*

Twenty-one consultants, including Sir Bertrand Dawson,
Sir Anderson Critchett, and Sir James Dundas-Grant,

---

[1] Barker himself believed that he owed his knighthood chiefly to the
Lord Chief Justice (Hewart).

received through the post a parody of a *Lancet* news item. Written by Viscount Northcliffe, founder of the *Daily Mail* and chief co-proprietor of *The Times*, it had been set up in print at his command by *Daily Mail* compositors.

A PROFITABLE COUGH

Considerable interest continues to be manifested in the well-known and profitable cough of Lord Northcliffe. Discovered in February 1918 by a general practitioner, it has from time to time been a source of much augmentation of income, not only to local medical men but also the consultants of Harley and Wimpole Streets.

The emoluments so profusely scattered have hitherto fallen into the hands of physicians, but we are glad to state that there is now a prospect of the surgical branch of the profession coming into its due share. Nursing home and massage circles are also looking forward to a proportion of the profits.

The attempts of one or two of the recipients at replying in a similar vein of facetiousness made embarrassing reading. A victim of obstinate laryngitis, Northcliffe had in the previous year paid £430 in doctors' bills. He told Dr Macnair Wilson, medical correspondent of *The Times*: 'Really, Harpole and Wimpley Streets make me laugh.' He wrote to his mother's doctor: 'In Harley Street, I went into one of those shops with four brass plates on its door, and my chauffeur, who is a very old friend of mine, said when I came out: "Did they all have a go at you, sir?" He asked the doctor to believe: "Had I followed your advice and stayed in bed at Totteridge I would have been well long ago." To the specialists he would say: "A glass of good Burgundy is better than all your tonics and quackcines".'

Health was a constant preoccupation of his life, and the medical correspondents of his newspapers had no more devoted reader. Dr Wilson of *The Times* knew what it was to be peremptorily summoned to take 'the Chief's' blood pressure at Printing House Square, or to sound his heart. Northcliffe made medicine 'news' in a way that it had never been before. He privately paid a Fellow of the Royal Society £250 a year in the hope that good might come of it for cancer sufferers. He gave £500 a year to Sir James Mackenzie's research institute at St Andrews. He helped a number of doctors through their personal financial crises.

His dire illness in 1922, with its accompaniment of rumours of sensational mental collapse, was diagnosed at first as 'disordered appendix'. On 19 June, Sir Thomas Horder was called in by Seymour Price, Northcliffe's physician since 1910. Horder's verdict was 'infective endocarditis', for which there was no known cure until the advent of penicillin nearly twenty years after. The malignant form it took in Northcliffe's case had only lately been recognised as a result of the work of Osler, Libman, the American pathologist, and Horder himself, who considered it 'the most insidious type of blood poisoning known to us'. The *British Medical Journal* surmised that Northcliffe had been menaced by the infection 'for at least a year'. Libman, who had been attending Madame Sarah Bernhardt in Paris, told Horder that he knew of seven recoveries. Buoyed up by the information, Northcliffe's brothers considered publicly offering a large cash sum for a cure, suggesting £25,000. Second thoughts questioned the wisdom of advertising the fact that the best medical advice in Britain was helpless, and the idea was dropped.

Instead, with Sir James Mackenzie's concurrence, Horder proposed a round-the-clock fresh air regime, 'a non-specific means to raise general resistance', and likely to be more effective, he believed, than any programme of bacteriotherapy. Permission was sought from the Duke of Devonshire, and obtained with the co-operation of Harold Macmillan, his son-in-law, for the use of the roof of the duke's town house, adjoining Northcliffe's, in Carlton Gardens, Pall Mall. There, in a hurriedly constructed shelter, Northcliffe passed the last terrible days of his fifty-seven years. By that time, the stories about his mental condition were exaggerated to the point at which it was generally accepted that he was mad. There was talk in medical circles of his being a victim of general paralysis of the insane. The inference was disproved by the Wassermann tests, supervised by Horder. Delirium was among the *sequelae* of later stages of the heart disease that had Northcliffe in its grip.

Horder saw his patient fifty-four times in seven weeks. He recalled to the present writer the much publicised episode in which Northcliffe denounced him as 'one of Lloyd George's bloody knights' and threatened him with a revolver. 'The weapon was not loaded.' Many people, including a fellow newspaper proprietor, Lord Beaverbrook, preferred to believe that it was. The patient was allowed to keep the revolver 'because it appeared to give him a sense of security'. Horder was equally firm in his assurance that the case presented no problem of insanity in the accepted or legal sense. Many people, again, persuaded themselves that there was a conspiracy to hide the truth. Their insistence appeared to be activated by an ill will that had its own morbid undertones.

*

A recession came to Harley Street in the 1920s. Bad trade and higher taxes were blamed. Many of the younger general practitioners had acquired new skills during their war service, and were able to give treatment and surgery that before the war had been beyond their competence. Out-of-town calls were a dwindling part of Harley Street practice. 'I used to spend a day or sometimes a week-end at, for example, Oxford, Northampton, Colchester, or Eastbourne, do one or sometimes three or four operations, and return with the fees in my pocket. Today all of these towns have well-equipped special departments in their own hospitals and have surgeons well-known in my specialty practising there, so that there is no need for the local doctors to call anyone from London.'[1]

The times were particularly hard on middle-aged doctors with no personal resources. There was keen if decently muted competition for hospital appointments. Many were glad of employment with the proliferating medical boards concerned

[1] R. Scott Stevenson: *In A Harley Street Mirror* (1951).

with war pension assessments. Attending one of them, the present writer had the unnerving experience of being nearly thrown out of a window by an overtaxed psychologist whose colleagues at the London Neurological Clinic had not realised until then that he was insane.

The war, which imposed open-air living on great numbers of both sexes, had done more than reduce the incidence of tuberculosis. It proved to many that the sedentary life is not consonant with total well-being. Gynaecologists reported the complete disappearance of chlorosis from their practices, other consultants an almost dramatic decline in the number of cases of articular gout, mucous colitis, and migraine. Harley Street was treating more hypertension, more endocrine disturbance, more trigeminal neuralgia, more diabetes, more gall bladder infection, more pernicious anaemia.

Private residence in the street was all but a thing of the past. General the Honourable Charles Strathavon Heathcote Willoughby, CMG, and Lady Muriel were still at 95, the Dowager Countess of Powerscourt at 97, Sir Kynaston Studd, a former Lord Mayor of London, at 67. The decline of domestic service, one of the most far-reaching social casualties of the First World War, meant the end of family life in Harley Street. There were no more dinner parties at No 85, where Dr Julius Pollock himself always brought up the wine from his cellar. One of his guests remembered that 'he would have only one bottle opened at a time and he always insisted on the cradle going round as the sun travels'.

George Cathcart, MA, MD, the bachelor consulting surgeon to the Throat Hospital, Golden Square, W., was continuing to entertain his friends at No 52. They included musicians— he was one of the original sponsors of the Promenade Concerts—actors, artists, diplomats, politicians, and the general practitioners who regularly sent him cases. His hospitality was that of one whose defiance of change was reinforced by ample private means. The memorable occasions he provided were recalled by Scott Stevenson, MD, FRCS of 31 Harley Street. 'I can see him sitting with a benevolent smile in his black velvet tuxedo at the head of the long table in his panelled dining-room. At either end of the room were cabinets lit by electricity, containing his collection of eighteenth-century glass, massive pieces of old Irish cut glass stood on the Sheraton sideboard, eight or ten candles in old glass candlesticks illuminating the table.'[1]

The son of a well-off Edinburgh wine merchant, Cathcart arrived in Harley Street in 1892 with a private income of £400 a year. In 1920, another laryngologist, Hunter Todd, of 11 Upper Wimpole Street, assured Scott Stevenson: 'No man can practice as a specialist in London unless he has a private income of at least £2,000 a year.' The new pattern of the consultant's life was a single room, or a suite, in Harley Street and a home in the suburbs.

*

Multiple room letting began at 88 Harley Street in the early post-war years when an elderly venereologist who feared a drop in income as a result of the propaganda of three national societies dedicated to the eradication of venereal diseases, fore-stalled the risk by subletting his rooms to fourteen other medical men. Soon afterwards the lessee of No 79 followed suit. It was the beginning of the new era in which names proliferated on the doors of Harley Street as lushly as on the stairways of the Middle Temple.

Single room rents averaged £300 a year on short tenancies. Plumbing was primitive. Up to the First World War, few of the houses had bathrooms. Usually, the house plans included what was known as a 'sanitary wing', a half-landing with a lavatory and space for a bath. Right up to the 1920s, some of the houses had no water supply above the ground floor.

Tenants were likely to meet unexpected difficulties when they wanted to assign their leases. Landlords had reservations about certain types of practitioner; for example, venereolo-gists and dermatologists. Patients of those specialists might give a 'bad impression' in the communal waiting-room.

[1] In an address to the College of Physicians of Philadelphia, 1957.

Patients posed another sort of risk. When Dr William Byam took over 92 Harley Street, he provided a cheerful open fire in his waiting-room. 'So many people would poke it to relieve their feelings. This led to dust and ashes being scattered in all directions.'[1] He had to replace the open grate by a gas fire. A reason for many Harley Street waiting-rooms being bare of ornament is that the consultants learnt long ago that not every kleptomaniac goes there to be cured.

An alleged patient called to see Dr Byam on a Saturday afternoon, professing to have a damaged shoulder that needed urgent treatment. The doctor's wife, who interviewed the caller in her husband's absence, noticed that he held his right arm stiffly by his side. After he had gone, she noticed also that a Chinese plate, one of a valuable pair, was missing from the waiting-room sidetable. Another trusting consultant who put a collection of *Everyman's Library* volumes in his waiting-room bookcase, lost them all. His copy of Macnaughton and Jones's *Diseases of Women* also vanished.

Dr J. Knox Campbell, addressing the Liverpool Medical Society, suggested that the erect posture in man is the un-recognised source of some of his worst afflictions, and recommended parents to encourage their children 'to revert to the all-fours position for a while each day'. He was complimented in print on having 'done good service' by Dr Harry Campbell, of Wimpole Street, whose observations suggested that 'char-women seem actually to enjoy the all-fours position adopted in scrubbing the floor'.

Less eccentric interest was shown in the 'fixation abscess' treatment of acute bacterial infection. Said to be used exten-sively on the Continent, the method consisted of subcutaneous inoculation by a minute quantity of turpentine to provoke the formation of a sterile abscess in the body tissue. The classic signs of inflammation were expected in twenty-four hours, an abscess developing in from four to six days. A small incision was then made, the pus extruded, and the wound dried up by hot fomentations. Theoretically, it produced a capillary

[1] *Dr. Byam in Harley Street* (Bles, 1962).

migration of the infective organism to the site of the abscess, where it was discharged. Recounting his experience of the treatment, Dr (now Sir) Adolphe Abrahams, 86 Brook Street, W. was cautious in approving it, while declaring himself ready 'to applaud any method which aims at converting a septicaemia into a localised focus of infection'.

The arrival in London of M. Emile Coue, the French pharmacist from Nancy, with his doctrine of auto-suggestion and his formula, 'Every day, in every way, I get better and better', had evangelical significance for the grey brotherhood of neurasthenics, their numbers augmented by the disturbing transition from war to peace. His press interviews produced many columns in the newspapers. That his system yielded a proportionate harvest of beneficial results was doubted. Dr William Brown, 88 Harley Street, presumably wished to check undue optimism by his authoritative reminder, as Wilde Reader of Mental Philosophy at Oxford University, that M. Coue 'offered nothing new'. More forceful critics said that the method intensified the paralysis of the will that characterised the types of patient to whom it appealed. Coue's answer was that he sought to bring the unconscious imagination into action as a more potent influence than will power.

The widespread interest in Coue's system, and its simplicity, was an inducement to medical men with languishing practices to venture into the comparatively new realm of psychological medicine. None of the higher medical diplomas was required. A room in Harley Street, a couch, a notebook; and any doctor with the humblest degrees could set himself up as a medical psychologist. 'Psychiatry offers a wonderful opening to the hyenas of Harley Street, the confidence men of medicine who trade on the goodwill and trust established by generations of honest men, who gamble on the magic of an address as able to suggest long training and established position.'[1]

Not all the opportunists were instinctively charlatans. Some were the victims of circumstance. *The Times* reported the

[1] Sir Heneage Ogilvie: *No Miracles Among Friends.*

'crisis in Harley Street', and published a daily column of letters from consultants, patients, and observers of the contemporary medical scene. General Bramwell Booth, head of the Salvation Army, wrote gratefully of specialists who gave their services freely in cases of hardship known to him. None the less, he thought that the prevailing scale of fees might be revised in the light of current stresses. Dr (later Sir) Ernest Graham-Little, 40 Wimpole Street, drew attention to the disparity in fees as between a physician and a surgeon, both in Harley Street, for two of his cases. The physician spent an hour with a patient and received 14 guineas. The surgeon performed an operation that had been carefully prepared for him in advance and for his half-hour's work went away with a cheque for 150 guineas.

'FRCS' told readers of *The Times*: 'A surgeon should give as little pain as possible while he is treating the patient, and no pain at all when he charges his fee.' A member of the Junior Army and Navy Club considered that 'no fees that are as elastic as those of Harley Street could ever be too high'. A. J. Walton, FRCS, of 5 Devonshire Street, W. wrote that 'it is remarkable how many wealthy men will willingly pay £2,000 for a motorcar, but will begrudge 150 guineas to the surgeon who has saved their lives'. There were renewed complaints about doctors with minor qualifications moving from general practice in the suburbs to Harley Street, trading on its prestige, and charging consultant fees. A patient appealed for 'a gentler manner and less brusqueness' among the specialists.

An anonymous surgeon stated that £4,000 a year was the minimum income on which a Harley Street reputation could be maintained. Writing from No 108, N. Bishop Harman, MA, FRCS, who was prominent in the internal affairs of the British Medical Association, intimated that it was the patients who required that 'we must be enshrined in suitable and substantial elegance'.

*

At nearly seventy, Sir William Arbuthnot Lane was a fine figure of a man with an authoritative presence that made those who knew him on Christian name terms feel that they were privileged. His reputation was a towering one. He was professionally respected as the only surgeon of his generation who could be relied on to open the abdomen safely. He was the first to do a radical mastoid operation, the first to accomplish heart resuscitation by massage through an abdominal incision, the first to use intravenous infusion. Sir Heneage Ogilvie also tells us that Lane had 'anatomical knowledge and manual skill that have never since been equalled'. He designed new surgical instruments. T. G. Layton, FRCS, said that 'you can almost trace Lane's thought over the years from old editions of instrument makers' catalogues'. His toothed forceps were the outcome of his preoccupation with the problem of haemostatic control. His operation wounds set a new standard for the surgeon's craft.

His family background was Ulster, his father an Army doctor. He went to school at Carmichael, Lanarkshire. 'Looking back on the education which the Scottish boy receives', he wrote, 'I am not surprised at the great success obtained by the men of this nation in the struggle for existence.'

At Guy's Hospital, London, he was a shy and solitary youth who found it 'most depressing' to wait in the famous Colonnade to join the the daily jostling procession of physicians, surgeons, and students into the wards. His subsequent career owed much to the apprenticeships he served in the lowly posts of ward clerk and assistant dresser before facing examinations. He was studious to the point of exhaustion. His mother saw him, 'many a time', with his head wrapped in cold compresses. He qualified in 1877, and appeared ever after to be dogged by a wish that he had opted for the career of a physician rather than of a surgeon. That he attained excellence in his chosen role reflected the determination with which he overcame his initial distaste for it.

He published a pamphlet called *Civilisation*, setting forth views that were the mainspring of his later fame as a surgeon. What he termed 'intestinal stasis, or delay in the passage of waste material through the bowels', was, in his opinion, the source of modern man's worst afflictions, including cancer, Addison's disease, rheumatoid arthritis, and obscurely morbid states of the blood. He described the toxic appearance of typical victims, drawing attention to the curious skin pigmentation that often accompanied it. The condition had been noted in the paintings of Burne-Jones; for example, in the *Golden Stair*, and in *Cophetua and the Beggarmaid*.

Alluding to 'the excellent work of Arbuthnot Lane', Dr Leonard Williams, one of Harley Street's livelier spirits, reaffirmed in a letter to *The Lancet* the view that 'the *causa causans* is the upright posture', leading to various forms of obstruction. 'An obvious remedy, therefore, would be for man to revert to the posture and gait of his quadruped ancestors, a reversion which, in many cases—those, for example, of Sir William Arbuthnot Lane's detractors—would be eminently suited to their intellectual capacities.' Dr Williams had no doubt that fasting one day a week was a more practical answer.

Trained in the Listerian tradition, Lane believed that the colon was the headquarters of a rampageous infective army, capable of doing untold damage through the bloodstream. Discarding the routine usage of calomel, creosote, and antiseptic enemas, he pronounced in favour of surgical extirpation. His colectomy operation, by which it was accomplished, brought him reputation, £10,000 a year, and abuse. *The Lancet* decided that he 'may have pushed his theories too far', but that he had 'brought to notice facts that were almost unknown or ignored before'.

The validity of Lane's judgment that the colon was a degenerate, useless, and treacherous part of the human organism was challenged at a meeting of the Royal Society of Medicine in 1922. J. P. Lockhart Mummery, a well-known cancer surgeon, did not agree that the healthy colon was 'a damnable heritage'. In his experience, colectomy patients suffered grave disadvantages. One was that they were deprived of the organ by which drugs were excreted; for example, morphia and arsenic, which became doubly toxic to the patients. Nor could he agree that intestinal stasis necessarily called for colectomy, although the operation was 'sometimes useful'.

Another speaker, E. G. Slesinger, had followed up fifty of Lane's total colectomies. He spoke of being 'amazed' at the results, which in many cases amounted to 'a resurrection'. E. Tyrell Gray cited physiological objections, and gave reasons why he had abandoned the operation 'for all but those cases where the colon was obviously seriously diseased'.

All heads were turned towards Arbuthnot Lane when he rose to speak. He agreed that 'it was a disgrace to medicine that colectomy for intestinal stasis should ever be necessary, but nevertheless the necessity frequently arose'. One of his recent cases was a Canadian ex-soldier who had had 'no less than sixteen abdominal operations'. The patient had 'toured the surgical clinics of North America'. At the celebrated Mayo Clinic, 'he was told that the only surgeon who could effect a cure in his case was Lane of England'. The patient was sent over to Lane. A total colectomy was done 'with extreme difficulty', because of complications. 'The man is now in perfect health, and working in the backwoods'. Lane then reiterated his faith that 'in experienced hands, the operation offers almost incalculable advantages in return for a comparatively small risk'.

The school that he may have dreamed of founding never gathered round him. He did not change his views or his methods, while insisting with even greater emphasis on 'two bowel movements a day' as a requisite of healthy living. He went on cutting out colons, and prescribing, at the same time, a large regular intake of liquid paraffin as a means of keeping beyond the abdominal surgeon's reach.

In his light grey frock-coat, always buttoned, he looked magisterial, urbane, self-satisfied. His carefully trimmed moustache, well arched eyebrows, and firm gaze, matched his logical mind. Some thought him a *poseur*, capable of the subtler insincerities. He was given to sarcasms that were not intended to hurt as much as they sometimes did. He was 'execrated or adored by his contemporaries according to their lights', says Sir Heneage Ogilvie, who insists that 'none could doubt his giant stature'. For many he was an inspiring teacher and an indomitable friend.

His courtesy was of the memorable kind, shown to all and sundry, and not switched on for effect. His old colleagues recall his characteristic way of addressing them 'with his head held a little to one side'. Talking on the telephone, he would invariably begin: 'Is that you? This is me.' Strictness in keeping appointments and dealing with correspondence was part of his formula for professional success. As far as he could ensure it, he answered every letter on the day of receiving it. Prominent in his personal routine was a daily walk of four miles in sunshine or in rain.

Patients calling on him in his prime at 21 Cavendish Square, where the Asquiths were his neighbours, often had to step over his black chow, lying proprietorially on the portico steps. A pet canary sat on the master's shoulder as he worked at his desk. A tame bullfinch had the liberty of the dining-room.

Some of Lane's colleagues, presuming him to be a rich man, were surprised that he continued in practice as long as he did. They were not to know that he had lost what might be thought a considerable fortune invested in Russian railways. Of greater importance to him was the satisfaction of knowing that he had retained his surgical mastery, that hand and eye had not lost their cunning. His vitality was unimpaired, and retirement for him was a happy compromise between fishing holidays on his property in Connemara and the rest of the year in London, preaching his gospel of sensible living.

His New Health Society was founded in 1925, 'with the object of improving the health, vigour, and happiness of the community and for the prevention of the diseases which are incident to civilization'.[1] Professionally, it meant that he, the surgeon, was a trespasser in the territory of the physician, and there was criticism of him for it. It became resentment when, pressing his campaign, he flouted the rule of anonymity and published a series of signed articles in the *Daily Mail*, urging

[1] *New Health Society Bulletin*, vol. 1, no. 1, January 1926.

less emphasis on the relief of effects and more on the removal of causes. Prevention was his watchword. When he had his name withdrawn from the Medical Register, he was not bowing to the storm but acquiring still wider freedom of action; for example, he allowed Harrods to use his name boldly in a half-page advertisement in the *Sunday Times* announcing that he had agreed to lecture on 'The Health Way to Happiness' at their store. 'We count ourselves fortunate in being able to present our patrons with the benefit of this world-famous doctor's experience, knowledge, and advice at first-hand.' He had an audience of 1,500.

His success on that occasion was followed by meetings in other parts of the country. At Oldham, Lancashire, three thousand people packed the hall, and many were carried out fainting, with mounted police controlling a disappointed crowd outside. Scott Stevenson said that Lane earnestly desired to have 'his then unorthodox ideas on nutrition, intestinal stasis, and the influence of sepsis on cancer causation, understood and accepted by the general public'.

No doubt Dr Leonard Williams received Lane's blessing when he proclaimed that 'the crime of our civilization is gluttony', the tyranny of mealtimes 'fantastic folly'. As for gluttony, 'the doctors all say we eat too much', wrote Sir Edward Cook, sometime editor of the *Westminster Gazette*, after dining with Sir Thomas Barlow, MD, at 10 Wimpole Street. 'My experience is that they do too.'

VIII

ABRAMS' BOX: TRUE OR FALSE?

The publication by the Hogarth Press in 1925 of the first two volumes of Freud's *Collected Papers* showed the vitality of his ideas compared with other therapeutic obssessions of the era. Guardedly, *The Lancet* conceded that 'the possibility is emerging that his place may indeed be among the pioneers'. The less durable enthusiasms were expressive of a society still fragmented by the explosive violence through which it had recently passed. Harley Street was being consulted about Dr Voronoff's rejuvenation treatment, and the Abrams Box.

Forty-four of Voronoff's case-sheets, published that year, suggested that senescence was being arrested by his method. They did not dispel doubts about the long-term results. Harley Street sent several well-known septuagenarians to be cured of testicular insufficiency at Voronoff's clinic on the Continent. A well-known Fleet Street special correspondent, Sir Perceval Phillips, told the present writer that he was 'horrified' by the change wrought in one of the patients known to him. Meanwhile, Voronoff's 'monkey gland' cult was a source of unrestrained hilarity in the music-halls. As for the Abrams Box, it induced scepticism rather than mirth.

Dr Albert Abrams, born 1869, practised as a neurologist at Sacramento Street, San Francisco. Observation of the work of Curie, Becquerel, and Röntgen, gave him the notion that all nature, including the human organism, was activated by an electrical force maintained at a certain level of power variable only by disease. Might it not be possible to measure the differentials and identify them with bodily states? Diagnosis would be followed by treatment on homeopathic principles applied to electricity, that like cures like. It was an adaptation of the theory of Hahnemann, the Viennese founder of homoeopathy, who believed that the potency of drugs exists not in their mass but in their energy.

Abrams constructed an instrument to warrant his thesis that 'the basis of disease is a disturbance of electronic equilibrium within the molecule'. Helped by the inventor of a device for detecting Zeppelins in the First World War, he produced what became notorious as the Abrams Box. It was an electrical apparatus by means of which he claimed to be able to tell from a specimen of blood or sputum the sex of the donor and the degree to which he or she was suffering from specific disease.

In spite of the confusing character of his claims, and his reckless use of terms borrowed from the vocabulary of electrical engineering, many believed that there was merit in the theory behind Abrams' Box, if not in his use of it. One of his champions was Conan Doyle, who had pronounced, in two articles contributed to *The Strand Magazine* (Dec. 1921–Jan. 1922), in favour of the existence of fairies. The creator of Sherlock Holmes said that Abrams was a genius. In that opinion he was supported by Sir James Barr, MD (1849–1938) sometime President of the British Medical Association. Sir James had recently published a pamphlet, *The Future of the British Race*, in which he deplored the nation's intellectual decline, and saw salvation only in a Comrades of the Great War movement, whose leaders would ensure that 'moral and physical degenerates would not be allowed to take any part in adding to the population'.

When Abrams began mass-producing his Box and entering into leasing arrangements with all and sundry, qualified or not, he fell foul of the powerful American Medical Association. His Box was vilified in the American press. Traps were set for him by unbelieving colleagues. One of the most widely publicised was the sample of blood from a Rhode Island Red rooster sent to Abrams by a Michigan physician, who received in return a diagnosis of congenital syphilis. An American scienti-

fic journal condemned the Box as 'a contraption which might
have been thrown together by a ten-year-old boy who knows a
little about electricity to mystify an eight-year-old boy who
knows nothing about it'.

In the judgment of F. A. Macquisten, KC, MP, who publicly
testified to the benefit that he and others known to him had
received from the Box, Dr Abrams was a victim of anti-
Semitism in the American medical profession. The *Jewish
World*, published in London, thought that a much stronger
influence was 'the blindness of organised science'.

The Abrams Box had a minor vogue in Harley Street in the
late '20s, adopted in good faith by a few experimentally-
minded practitioners, exploited like a fruit machine for its
profitability by a few others. A doctor with Irish degrees,
practising at the north end of Harley Street and known to
be in straitened circumstances, took up the Box and was soon
able to look his bank manager in the eye again. A colleague
remembers calling on him and, in his absence from the room,
taking a quick glance at his appointment book. 'He was seeing
seventy patients a week.'

In that same period, a diagnostic apparatus developed *de
novo* by W. S. Boyd, MD, of Sandyford Place, Glasgow, was
tested by a committee of doctors and scientists under the
chairmanship of Sir Thomas Horder. It was known as Boyd's
Emanometer. The committee tested the Abrams Box within
the same terms of reference. Horder lectured on their findings
at the Royal Society of Medicine. A doctor who was present
considered the lecture 'one of the most extraordinary and
tantalising communications ever presented before a scientific
society'.[1]

The tests of Boyd's Emanometer were carried out in conditions which, according to Horder, Abrams had always
evaded. Abrams, the committee's report stated, 'put forward
startling claims on the slenderest evidence, using the jargon
characteristic of charlatans', and employing equipment that

[1] J. H. Douglas Webster, MD, radiologist, of Chandos Street, Cavendish
Square, in *The Lancet*, 17 January 1925.

was 'crudely made and imperfectly developed'. Granting the possibility 'that Dr Abrams might have lighted upon a discovery of genuine scientific importance', the Horder committee dismissed his work as being of no scientific account, and regretted the unwillingness of those using his Box in England to provide opportunities for tests under acceptable conditions.

Dr Boyd, of Glasgow, concentrated on experiments with electro-physical phenomena in relation to homoeopathic medicine. The Horder committee was satisfied that his 'meter of emanations' registered a hitherto undetected state of energy. He submitted his device to more than one stringent test, the last being considered 'a very successful demonstration'. Specimens of blood, sputum, tears, and other secretions were placed on filter paper in different envelopes. The problem for Dr Boyd was to pair them correctly by the use of his Emanometer.

The result was 'singularly impressive'. The committee agreed that 'certain substances, when placed in proper relation to the Emanometer of Boyd, produced, beyond any reasonable doubt, changes in the abdominal wall of the "subject" of a kind which may be detected by percussion'. Sir Thomas Horder and Dr C. B. Heald, a pioneer of electrotherapy, both submitted themselves to experiment and confirmed that particular finding.[1] No evidence was forthcoming to suggest that electronics was likely to make a significant contribution to pathology, 'the bedrock of medicine'. Horder himself was by no means unsympathetic to the theories they had been investigating. He told his son: 'I hesitate to talk about vibrations, since so little is known of these things, but there is something of that about it all.'

Boyd's ideas continue to be a subject of investigation by the medical research institute at Glasgow that bears his name, by the de la Warr organisation at Oxford, and by dedicated private inquirers like Dr W. Ritchie McCrae, of 43 Devonshire

[1] *A Preliminary Communication Concerning the 'Electronic Reactions' of Abrams, with special reference to the 'Emanometer' Technique of Boyd.* (Bale, Sons & Danielson, 1925.)

Street, London, W., who has made his own refinements of the techniques, resulting, it is claimed, in enhanced accuracy of diagnosis. The subject remains outside the pale of scientific orthodoxy, the isolation of its exponents, one is tempted to think, akin to that of John Logie Baird, the television pioneer, who was engaged in his first tentative experiments at Hastings in those same years.

Writing of the 'wonderful and delicate energy' that engaged the interest of Boyd, Dr Ritchie McCrae reminds us that 'no flower gave its fabulous scent without first taking its origin from the wonder in its seed'.[1] He remains staunch in his belief that the physicists will eventually pick up and develop the present tenuous lines of research along which he and other followers of Boyd are still working in steadfast hope and faith.

*

Sir James Mackenzie, the heart specialist who disliked that ascription, had realised his hope of release from the trammels of Harley Street and, with heroic firmness of purpose, had set up his Institute of Clinical Research at St Andrews. It was dedicated to bringing the methods of research into concert with the work of the ordinary doctor; in short, to the reformation of general practice, and for its founder it meant a heavy personal sacrifice. Giving up his West End work, Mackenzie also resigned as head of the cardiac department organised for him by Lord Knutsford at the London Hospital. His reputation went before him at St Andrews; yet he was personally un-known there except to one or two medical colleagues. From the start, he was harassed by financial and administrative problems. He had contributed substantially to the Institute from his own pocket. Within a few months of his arrival in Scotland, he realised that he was marked down as a victim of the heart disease on which he was a world authority, angina pectoris. (His parson brother had died of it in the pulpit.) With quiet fortitude, he resumed his role of private consultant,

[1] See his *Summary of Forty Years' Study of Potency Energy*, a paper read to the Faculty of Homeopathy, 23 March 1961.

travelling widely to see patients in many parts of Scotland, often to London, and several times to the Riviera. He accepted all the lecture engagements offered to him, and wrote numerous articles for the professional journals. He recast his definitive work on heart diseases, and wrote another book on the form of it that was killing him: 'a most sinister comment on the life-work of the greatest heart specialist in the world'.[1] The main purpose of those efforts was to provide for the continuance of the work at St Andrews.

He measured what remained of his life span by his performance at golf on the most renowned of courses. 'When he first came to St Andrews, he could play two rounds without distress. After a time, he could play only one round. Then only nine holes. And then, so soon, only a single hole.'[2] He paid a last professional visit to London, telling a friend at the Reform Club: 'I've promised my wife that I won't do it again. The fee I was offered might make a bit of difference—the Institute needs every penny.'

His work was done. He gave up his directorship of the Institute, and retired to London, ending his days in a flat at Albert Hall Mansions. He told Dr Wilson: 'A man with angina pectoris is like one of those old martyrs, confined in a room the walls of which gradually folded inwards and crushed him.'

*

Sir Herbert Barker, in his middle fifties, was preparing to indulge his dream, as a sunlover, of spending the rest of his years at ease on some delectable Mediterranean shore. His practice had never been conducted according to a scale of fees. In general, he charged what the patient could afford to pay. He was understood to have received five hundred guineas for an operation, and known to charge as little as five guineas for applying the same degree of skill. His letter files show that in numerous instances he gave his services free.

It was an occasion for visiting Dr Axham, who was then

[1] Arnold Bennett: *The Savour of Life* (1928).
[2] R. Macnair Wilson: *The Beloved Physician* (1926).

living in the south London suburb of Norbury. Barker saw at once that his old colleague's remaining years were likely to be few. Enfeebled, the doctor spent most of his time in his dressing-gown, huddled in an armchair as if shrinking from further experience of life, which had treated him so harshly. 'Infamous conduct—infamous conduct!' he went on whispering to himself, seemingly still unable to grasp the enormity of the verdict that had been given against him nearly fifteen years before. Through them all he had been sustained by his wife's devoted care. Barker remembered that in earlier days 'she was a most beautiful woman'.

Axham's place as anaesthetist to Barker had been filled by Frank Collie, MD, a retired colonial medical officer of health whose brother, Sir John Collie, MD, author of *The Psychology of the Fraudulent Mind* (1913), exclaimed when he heard what was afoot: 'You're going to work with that damned quack? Don't be a fool!' Frank Collie cheerfully risked the displeasure of the governing body, which, significantly, took no formal notice of his breach of the code against 'covering' an unqualified man, the technical offence that had been Axham's undoing. Before appointing Collie, Barker had made it known, with deliberate intent, that he was seeking a qualified anaesthetist to succeed Axham. 'I was inundated with letters from medical men offering their services.'

A new attempt was made to remove the stigma from Axham's name. The case for doing so was re-stated by Barker's former patient, J. B. Capper, of *The Times*, in a letter printed in that newspaper. Capper wrote that he was not less indebted to Axham than to Barker for benefit received at the latter's hands. 'Dr Axham may well be thought to have suffered sufficiently for his technical fault, if fault there were. Let the GMC, if they so please, regard the obliteration of the brand of "infamy" as an act of grace. Dr Axham is too old to resume practice; no possible harm could be done. Must a sentence passed by the General Medical Council, unlike most of those pronounced by Courts of Justice in the name of the King, necessarily endure for life?'

Admiral Lord Charles Beresford offered to raise the matter in the House of Commons. John Murray, the publisher, wrote to *The Times* urging that Axham's medical degrees should be restored. 'It would give great pleasure to the old man, and could only do credit to the Council.' Sir Herbert Parsons, director of a firm of wholesale chemists, also wrote to *The Times*, stating his opinion that Barker's knighthood 'constituted one of the greatest triumphs of sheer worth over prejudice ever recorded', and reminding readers that it was Dr Axham who, 'in the early days of the then Mr Barker's struggles, recognised the merits of his operations and made them painlessly possible'. Barker thought it 'something of a bombshell for the doctors' when Sir Bertrand Dawson took his stand with Axham's supporters.

The Registrar of the General Medical Council, Dr Norman King, unwisely revived memories of the lawsuit that nearly wrecked Barker's career in 1911. He was publicly rebuked by John Murray in another letter to *The Times*, which disclosed that Axham had received 'a suggestion from the GMC' that he should apply for the restoration of his name to the Register. 'Practically the entire responsible press was now fighting for the re-instatement of my colleague', Barker wrote. 'The result of the appeal to the Royal College of Surgeons was awaited by the public with growing—almost menacing—impatience and and the intensest interest.'

The *Church Times* recorded 'a widespread feeling that a tribunal entirely professional in its membership, and from whose decisions there is no appeal, is sometimes influenced by narrow and antiquated points of view. In such cases, its findings are a hindrance to the existence of that perfect medical service necessary for the public well-being' (4 December 1925). *The Tablet*, associating itself 'heartily with the movement on Dr Axham's behalf', put the question: Does not this affair illustrate once more the slowness of our Protestant fellow-countrymen to understand the power of dispensation? Not even the Pope of Rome himself could dispense the most powerful Prince from obedience to any law of God; but the rules and regulations which men have made can also be relaxed by men, according to circumstances' (12 December 1925). 'A code of etiquette which causes an aged and respected physician to be struck off the Register for aiding a famous alleviator of suffering like Sir Herbert Barker is on a par with that which would prevent a citizen rescuing a drowning woman because they had not been introduced' (*John Bull*, 12 December 1925).

Barker had appealed personally to the President of the General Medical Council, Sir Donald MacAlister, begging him to show clemency to 'a frail old man, now over 80'. He received a *pro forma* reply intimating that if Axham filled in the necessary papers the matter would be given attention. 'A trifle chilled', Barker wrote, 'I set the machinery in motion.' When Axham heard of it, 'he showed great joy'.

Hope was crushed in him when on 15 January 1926, *The Times* announced that the Council of the Royal College of Surgeons had considered the appeal, and did not 'see fit to rescind the resolution of 13 July 1911, removing Mr Axham from being a member of the College'. The General Medical Council came to a similar decision. 'The press flared into righteous anger' (Barker). The *Daily Mail* printed the names of the members of the Council, 'so that each may ask himself whether he is proud of having treated Dr Axham thus'. *The Lancet* thought that there was 'a case for clemency'.

The pressure of public opinion was such that Sir Bertrand Dawson was invited to give his views, as a leader of the medical profession, to sixty members of both Houses of Parliament on 24 February 1926. When someone complained that Sir Herbert Barker had not been encouraged to demonstrate his methods, Dawson answered that there was nothing to stop an unqualified man opening a clinic for poor persons, 'where those interested could come and watch him at work'. He could not regard Barker as a pioneer, 'when Great Britain is the proud possessor of the man of genius in manipulative surgery whose reputation is world-wide as thinker, investigator, and leader—I refer to Sir Robert Jones'. He did not point out, what presumably he knew, that Jones's pre-eminent reputation as an orthopaedic surgeon rested on a foundation of training given him by an unqualified practitioner, Owen Thomas, a renowned bonesetter, who was his uncle.

*

A different temper prevailed in Scotland. The Royal College of Physicians of Edinburgh, of which Axham had been a licentiate, restored his professional status within their comity on the ground that he had abstained 'for the last five years from the practices which led to his suspension, and will not resume them'. Axham could call himself 'Dr' again. Reading the announcement in the evening papers, Barker 'laughed outright', reflecting that 'those canny Scots' had spoilt a generous action 'by this latest kick at me and my poor anaesthetist'. None the less, he shared the general satisfaction. 'My telephone started ringing about 9 p.m. and continued till 2 a.m. almost uninterruptedly.'

The next morning he went down to Norbury to see Axham again. 'How happy he and his wife were! The look of sadness had left his fine old face, and an expression of new hope was alight in his eyes. He could not speak for a minute—emotion choked him. He just held my hand and looked at me.' Barker had brought a bottle of champagne. 'We're going to drink your health and congratulate you on this great and eventful day.'

Dr Axham had become a public figure again at the age of eighty. 'The reason is to be found in the national sense of fair play', said *The Times* (9 April 1926). From his fading memory, the old doctor recalled to Barker a happening at one of the big London hospitals. A knee was opened by a surgeon for presumed tubercular infection. 'A slight derangement of the internal cartilage was found—the sort of thing you'd have put right in a minute by manipulation. To crown the blunder', Axham continued, 'the patient died after the unnecessary operation. Now I wonder what would have happened to you if *you* had been the guilty party.' Barker listened with quiet

Lord Horder in his consulting-room at 141 Harley Street.

Above : George Bernard Shaw lunches with Sir Herbert Barker at the Dorchester Hotel, London, 1937. In the 1950s, the *British Medical Journal* reported a recession in Harley Street. *Below :* A consulting-room at 13 Harley Street.

patience. He had heard Axham tell the story too often before.

The action of the Royal College of Physicians of Edinburgh removed the technical barrier to the replacement of Axham's name on the Medical Register. A *Manchester Guardian* leading article declared that 'the Physicians have in this matter shown themselves more in touch with the realities of justice than the Surgeons'. *The Nation* had no doubt that the Edinburgh physicians had 'averted the storm of public opinion which was rapidly gathering against medical trade unionism'. There was a widespread expectation of a change of heart by the General Medical Council.

Himself more hopeful of that prospect than he had been for many years, Axham wrote a last earnest and pathetic appeal to the Council to give heed to his advanced age and declining strength, and to call an early meeting at which his case could be finally reconsidered. His request was not granted. The next Council meeting, he was informed, was fixed for May 1926 and it could not be brought forward. He died on 8 April 1926, in his eighty-seventh year. His last words, recorded by his wife, were: 'I forgive as I hope to be forgiven.'

Sir Bruce Bruce-Porter spoke out against 'the terribly depressing effect' on Dr Axham of the General Medical Council's long delay in considering his appeal. 'In my opinion, that delay militated against his chances of recovery from his recent illness.' Sir William Arbuthnot Lane was 'dreadfully sorry. It is in the nature of a tragedy', which he thought might do good by bringing home to the General Medical Council 'the need to revise their rules'. Sir William Milligan, one of the great provincial specialists, thought it 'most unfortunate that the GMC did not hold a special meeting to reconsider Dr Axham's case'. To him it seemed 'almost inhuman that no attempt was made to soothe the last days of one who, although guilty of a technical offence, had acted in the interests of suffering humanity'.

Sir Herbert Barker was at Alassio when he heard of Axham's

death. He was too ill to travel home for the funeral at Mitcham, Surrey. In the congregation of about twenty persons were Arbuthnot Lane and John Murray, the publisher. Lane afterwards wrote to Barker: 'I went to that funeral with sadness and horror at the way he was treated by eminent representatives of my profession. I do not remember seeing any other of his colleagues at that sad event.'

Returning to London later that spring, Barker had a letter from Sir Alfred Fripp, of 19 Portland Place, W., who wrote: 'I have three cases that I want to talk to you about. Most of all, I want to see you and to talk about yourself.' Across the foot of the letter, Barker scribbled in happy surprise: 'The King's surgeon—*what* a change! ! !'

*

Sir Alfred Fripp was extraordinary in a sense not implied by his Court appointment. No other surgeon of his eminence combined a more intense professional and social life. His diary tells of his performing an hysterectomy involving the removal of a fibroid growth of 6¾ lb, and, after 'scrubbing down', hurrying off to an At Home given by Madame Melba, 'who sang divinely'. He left an operating table tragedy for 'a weekend party at Gerald Balfour's', where he met a lady who, forty-eight hours afterwards, arrived in his Harley Street consulting-room 'with a growth that was her death sentence'.

An ardent first-nighter, he saw the opening performance of *A Cricket on the Hearth* at the Garrick Theatre, and drove straight from it to Guy's Hospital to do four midnight operations, seven the next day, nine the next, and the following day 'rushed up to Nottingham to see a patient and got home at 2 A.M. Very hard work, £800.' Another morning he removed five appendixes, 'including the Countess Gleichen's, completing £1,000 in eleven days'.

Like Sir Frederick Treves, he was a Dorset man, born at Blandford, the son of an artist whose watercolours were regularly exhibited in the London galleries. While at Guy's as a dresser, preparing for his finals, Fripp informed a fellow student: 'I'm going to the top or nowhere.' The remark helped to fasten on him his reputation as a man of the world.

He first put up his plate at 65 Harley Street, sharing rooms with his physician brother-in-law, William (later Sir William) Hale-White. When he was thirty-one, he married a girl aged sixteen. Soon he was earning a thousand a year and in a position to set himself up more sumptuously at 19 Portland Place, W. His success at court, originating in his attendance on the Duke of Clarence, brother of the future King George V, continued Harley Street's link with the Throne established by Queen Victoria's physicians. Fripp's social interests included friendships with famous stage personalities, notably Irving and Tree. By his biographer's testimony, 'he was the actors' surgeon *par excellence*. He knew the profession intimately, and attended them with tireless zeal, generally refusing remuneration. They were often terrible patients, and caused endless trouble.'[1]

Knighted for his services to Army medicine in the South African war, he claimed to have 'refused baronetcies from more Prime Ministers than any other living man'. For all that he had access to the highest social circles, he objected to hereditary titles, and that prejudice hardened with the years. 'I worship few,' he wrote in his diary, 'I bow down to none.' In the political arena, his hero was Stanley Baldwin, the Prime Minister.

As a consulting surgeon, he always placed his women patients with their backs to the light. His domestic staff and secretary were trained to the special discipline of never raising their voices, tapping lightly on his consulting-room door, closing it gently, appearing unhurried in all circumstances.

He told a succession of students at his old hospital, Guy's, that 'kindness is often more desirable in a doctor than efficiency', and warned them never to 'let a word escape you which might cause a patient misery'. It was better to speak of 'heart weakness' than of 'heart disease', because patients are easily frightened, 'especially by words like "chronic" and "malignant".' After all, he would say, 'such expressions are

[1] Cecil Roberts: *Alfred Fripp* (1932).

frequently only opinions'. He would add: 'Of course we all have to die, but we don't have to be frightened as well.' Another of his medical axioms was: 'Always keep a dying patient's relatives busy.'

Through many years he taxed himself to the limit. Fully aware of it, he took to his bed for the last time in January 1930, overwhelmed by tiredness, and having written on a slip of paper: 'My number is up. I must go.' A codicil to his will endowed a public lecture to be given annually under the title, 'Happiness'. The effort of putting his signature to it exhausted him. He had written some last thoughts a day or two previously. 'So this is my exit! Well, what a lot of other times, places, and ways it might have occurred in.' His reflections on death led him to believe that 'it is not obliteration, nor is it the separation from our dear ones for ever. Fancy,' he wrote in those last hours, 'if one lost one's only chance of dying!' His chance came on 25 February 1930. He was sixty-five. His diaries, that may have been of exceptional social and professional interest, have unaccountably vanished.

The old Italians held that the good surgeon must have the eye of an eagle, the heart of a lion, and the hands of a woman. If those requirements were not immaculately combined in the person of Sir Alfred Fripp, he was an abundantly able exponent of a craft that came to maturity in his lifetime. To that culmination he made a notable contribution of character, courage, and skill.

IX

KIPLING CALLS IN BARKER

Sir Herbert Barker's withdrawal from his practice in Park Lane had been treated as a newsworthy event. His retirement was more than nominal and yet far from final. Urgent demands continued to be made on him by people of all sorts and conditions. His vigour was diminished, his skill not, and his ardour for making use of it, and his compassion, impelled him again and again to forego the leisure that he had planned.

Augustus John kept in touch with him on general health matters, apparently preferring Barker's advice to that of the medical experts. So did Shaw, whose wife had become a patient of Barker's after a car accident caused by Shaw's bad driving. Shaw wrote to Barker about 'the new exercises' that Barker had recommended to him. 'I was puzzled by the absence of all stiffness.' He described in a letter to Barker his daily performance in the swimming bath at the Royal Automobile Club, Pall Mall. 'One of my tricks is to hang in the water, floating almost vertically with my face (not my ears) just above the surface.' By that means he relaxed far more completely 'than is possible in contact with a floor'. He was in his eightieth year. As part of the exercise, 'I stiffen and hoop myself backwards, stretching from the small of my back to the tips of my hair and toes; a real strychnine stretch' (2 June 1931).

'I should love to come and see you and learn and practise those long-life exercises of yours', Augustus John told Barker, whom he knew familiarly as 'Boneo'. 'You have always done me good, and I feel it is high time that I put myself in your hands again' (17 September 1931). 'I think he should form a health colony', John told Lady Barker. 'I am much better for the treatment and exercises he taught me. All my aches and pains have gone' (18 March 1932).

Considering the number of appeals for help that he still received, it seemed to Barker more important than ever that his manipulative methods should become the common property of the medical profession. It was nearly thirty years since he had first offered to demonstrate them 'before a committee of surgeons' (1906). The offer was 'received with scorn and derision', as he reminded readers of *The Times* in 1932.

His friend Basil Peto, who championed him in Parliament, proposed a Barker Gold Medal to be given in commemoration of his services in war and peace. A grateful potentate who was his patient, the Maharajah Kumar of Kutch, had given £1,000 for the purpose. Peto took Barker to discuss the proposal with Arthur Greenwood, Minister of Health in the second Labour Government (1929). Lord Moynihan, then President of the Royal College of Surgeons, was present in the Minister's room. When Peto outlined the scheme, Moynihan 'almost spluttered with indignation' (Peto). If a gold medal was to be given to anyone for manipulative surgery, it should go to Sir Robert Jones, the famous orthopaedic surgeon of Liverpool and London. Looking sternly at Barker, Moynihan said: 'He has done far more and far better work than you have ever done.' Peto thought it 'a rude and brutal thing to say', and turned his thoughts to the possibility of 'a Barker Chair of Manipulative Surgery at Oxford or Cambridge'. In the years to come, Barker had good cause to remember Moynihan's outburst, which Moynihan himself may have preferred to forget.

To the Editor of The Medical Press and Circular:

17 August 1932

Sir,—In the report of the Section of Physical Medicine, held at the Centenary Meeting of the British Medical Association, I notice that the president, while deprecating the lack of appreciation of the value of manipulation, went on to say that 'the failure of the bonesetter is generally due to faulty diagnosis'. From a very wide experience of the methods of manipulative surgery outside the hallowed gates of orthodoxy, may I be allowed to state most emphatically that the converse is much more in accordance with the truth?

I have seen some 5,000 cases of knee joints, tennis elbows, flat feet, and many other conditions, treated by manipulation with complete and permanent success. I would not care to say how many of those cases had sought aid from an unqualified practitioner as a result of faulty diagnosis by a registered practitioner. There were hundreds.

To me it is deplorable that all the discussions of the value of manipulative surgery at the BMA meeting ignored the man[1] whose work is responsible for manipulative surgery now being recognised in every hospital in London. We claim to be a broadminded profession. In nothing so much as this question of giving credit to the pioneer of manipulative surgery does this claim fail.

I am, Sir,
Yours faithfully,

Hove, Sussex. FRANK COLLIE, MD

Rudyard Kipling wrote to tell Barker that he was 'in great distress' about his wife who, for several years, had been suffering from the presumed effects of a fall. X-ray pictures suggested a displacement of the lumbar vertebrae. He asked Barker, 'if you could, of your kindness, make it possible to see her' (1 May 1934).

Preparing to take his wife to The Grove, St Lawrence, Jersey, where Barker was living while waiting to move his household to Spain, Kipling wrote saying that he himself was '*very* far from well' (2 August 1934). He had long been in the care of Sir John Bland-Sutton, sometime president of the Royal College of Surgeons, who 'could never relieve his abdominal pain',[2] and who was the original of Sir James Belton in one of Kipling's last short stories, *The Tender Achilles*.

---

[1] Barker's name, which appeared in Dr Collie's letter to the editor, was suppressed in the printed version.
[2] *Rudyard Kipling*, by Charles Carrington (Macmillan, 1955).

Kipling made a speech at a dinner of The Royal Society of Medicine in which he suggested that occult influences would be integrated in the medicine of the future. What gave his contacts with Barker special interest was not his implied desertion of orthodox medicine but the fact that they occurred when he was inferentially exposed to severe, and even desperate, psychic stress. It was the period during which he wrote *Hymn of Breaking Strain*, with its theme of the burdens 'too merciless to bear' that the gods put upon men. A biography, as yet unpublished, is authoritatively said to record an attempt at suicide made by him in his last years. His letters to Barker, written within two years of his death, show no sign of infirmity of hand or spirit, except the last of them, dated December 1935.[1]

A Bill that would require osteopaths to be registered and regulated was coming before Parliament. Kipling told Barker that he did not believe that it would go through, and asked Barker whether he was ready to bet on it. In due course, he took 'the wife' to see Barker in Jersey, and a little while after reported that she was walking '*much* better'. At the same time, Barker prescribed bran for Kipling's acidity, and Kipling commented that 'it makes one feel *cleaner* inside'. He hoped that the Barkers would visit them at Bateman's, Burwash, Sussex. 'We want to show you this little valley,' and he signed the letter 'with renewed gratitude and warmest wishes.' A postscript asked whether 'the wife's' depression could be due to the breaking up of uric acid in her system (8 September 1934). He had given Barker a collected edition of his works, each volume autographed, one with the added inscription: 'He who is sick let him fall into the *hands* of the physician.'

Later that year, Kipling consulted Barker about 'the wife's sugar-trouble', depression, and diet. He hoped that if Barker was coming to London in the near future, he would have 'a look at her again' (28 November 1934). Apropos an otherwise unrecorded syndrome, Shaw wrote to Barker: 'I dropped down dead at just the right moment, and then very stupidly

[1] See page 131.

revived again and slept for three days. Most annoying' (7 December 1934). Three years later, Shaw, the lifelong vegetarian, was an unwilling patient of Harley Street specialists, who treated him, successfully, for pernicious anaemia.

*

Tired by the years of extraordinary exertion and frustration, Barker was an ailing man in the '30s. When he faced an operation for prostate trouble, his advisers and well-wishers rallied round. Dawson of Penn recommended three surgeons: Jocelyn Swann, 75 Wimpole Street; J. Swift Joly, 80 Harley Street; S. G. MacDonald, 51 Queen Anne Street. Sir Ernest Graham-Little, MD, MP, dermatologist, 40 Wimpole Street, proposed Frank Kidd, FRCS, 55 Harley Street. Endorsing the recommendation of S. G. MacDonald, Sir Robert Armstrong-Jones, MD, FRCS, added the flattering thought that 'there would be great public dissatisfaction if you were left to suffer without the help of the best advice'.

Before making his choice, Barker heard from Lord Moynihan at Leeds: 'I very strongly believe in prostatectomy, or some of its newer modifications.' He supplied a footnote to surgical history. 'I helped with the first case ever done, in Leeds, when I was a dresser. We have a parental interest in the operation, and have done more than any other place in the world, with unsurpassed success.'

Still anxious, Barker sent a questionnaire to Sir John Lavery, RA, who had recently undergone a prostatectomy. Describing his experience of the two anaesthetics used, he looked back 'with horror'. He commended the operation, despite its immediate after effects, which were 'simply hell'. His recovery was complete; he was 'a happy man again'.

For further reassurance, Barker wrote to Kenneth Walker, of 149 Harley Street, who specialised in partial prostatectomies, and who was also an experienced psychologist. Walker replied: 'I am going to answer your letter very fully. I detect an undercurrent of worry beneath it.' Barker could fairly count it as part of his success that so much goodwill was being shown to him in Harley Street.

*

In his letter, Kenneth Walker touched on a matter that was amplifying Barker's current worries. On 11 December 1934, Viscount Elibank asked the House of Lords to give a second reading to the Osteopaths' Bill. It had been twice before the House of Commons, 'where it could not be proceeded with owing to pressure of other business' (Hansard). After a debate in which Moynihan and Dawson of Penn opposed the Bill, the House of Lords referred it to a Select Committee, with power to call witnesses.

Not only in the public mind was there a mistaken identification of osteopathy with manipulative surgery. A number of MPs supposed that they were 'one and the same'. Non-medical members of the House of Lords imagined that the Bill was a revival of 'the Barker controversy'. Graham-Little wrote that 'the osteopaths have encouraged that confusion, their most valuable asset' (*Daily Telegraph*, 26 January 1935). Barker wrote to *The Times*, marking the boundaries between himself and the osteopaths, and supporting the Bill. That he did so was considered 'an illogical action' by a vice-president of the British Medical Association, Sir Henry Brackenbury, MD. Sir Henry regarded the osteopaths' claim to cure 'most of the ills that flesh is heir to' by manipulating the spine as 'an anatomical and physical absurdity'.

Barker may have wished that he had stood aside from the controversy when it touched acrimony with the publication of a letter in *The Lancet* from Denis Browne,[1] a rising young orthopaedic surgeon, of 48 Queen Anne Street. Browne urged his medical colleagues to remove 'the one eternal jibe at our profession', namely, that it wilfully ignored 'any advance originating outside its own members'. He wanted osteopathy discussed before a jury of laymen 'of the type of Julian Huxley, J. B. S. Haldane, C. E. M. Joad, or Malinowski'. He fore-

---

[1] Knighted 1961.

saw that the net result of such an enquiry might be the acknowledgment of 'a small residue of original work'. Let a similar jury, he proposed, investigate the results achieved by Sir Herbert Barker. 'Could it be doubted that his reputation would be lower, that his magician's powers would have shrunk to a meagre repertoire with results as variable as our own? Deprived of the halo of persecution he and all the other wonder-workers would shine far less brightly in the public eye?' For peroration Browne added that he was 'sick of seeing the profession behaving like the lions in Trafalgar Square. Can't it turn round and bite?' (26 January 1935).

Barker was upset. 'Ye gods!' he wrote. 'Every chapter of my life proves this view to be a lie.' He begged a friend to write 'a line of indignation' to *The Lancet* in reply to Browne. Sir Robert Armstrong-Jones, writing independently to *The Lancet* from North Wales, protested against 'the nasty and confused letter of personal invective published over the name of Mr Denis Browne', considering it 'unfortunate, apparently malicious, and unjustifiable, its only redeeming feature its humour in the selection of the jury named'. The editor of *The Lancet* thought that it would be 'a pity' to publish Sir Robert's reply, and courteously declined to do so.

A Wimpole Street specialist in nervous diseases, J. S. Risien Russell, shared Barker's 'feelings of indignation'. *The Lancet* found space for a comment from one of Harley Street's best known orthopaedic men, A. S. Blundell Bankart, who wrote that he knew a woman who had spinal manipulation by an osteopath for eighteen months—'for flat-foot!' In his judgment, the Osteopaths' Bill was 'a purely American stunt' designed to establish for the osteopaths a monopoly of all manipulative surgery. 'They are relying on public feeling aroused by the Barker controversy for the success of their venture.'

Sending copies of the correspondence about the Bill to Robert Blatchford, sometime editor of *The Clarion*, literary organ of radical Socialism, Barker parenthetically touched on a more esoteric subject, in which Blatchford was actively interested. 'Spiritualism?' Blatchford replied. 'Well; I cannot break down the evidence. The case seems to be sound. I hope the claim is true, but as a mere man, conscious of his unworthiness, I feel the hope is too good to be true. We shall know some day—*perhaps*' (5 February 1935). J. L. Garvin, editor of *The Observer*, wished that he and Barker 'could have a personal talk'. 'As a layman,' he felt himself to be at a disadvantage in discussing the Osteopaths Bill. Suggesting that Barker should set out the facts in an article, 'without violence or libel' that ebullient editor paid him the tribute: 'Not only by gifts, but proofs, you are a great man' (6 February 1935).

*

Kipling reported to Barker on 31 March 1935 that his wife's leg was better. She had walked on a hill-road near Bateman's for nearly half an hour—'that's *you*'. He asked Barker to send his views on the Osteopaths Bill—'typed if possible', more than likely, a reflection on Barker's thick-nibbed handwriting. Barker was going to his villa at Churriana, Malaga, to rest after his operation. In Kipling's opinion, expressed in the letter, Spain was moving to the Right. He would not be surprised by a return to the monarchy within five years. He was sorry about Barker's operation. The prostate gland was an organ that gave more trouble 'than most of the other gadgets which it has pleased the Almighty to fit us up with'.

Six weeks later, he wrote again. 'The wife' wanted Barker to deal with a pain in her neck. It was a kind of neuritis, and it affected her hearing. 'Goodness knows, she doesn't need *that* added to her troubles' (17 May 1935). He himself had not been 'quite fit', he wrote later in the year. 'The wife's' diabetic trouble was 'very obstinate'. He signed himself on that occasion, 'Ever most sincerely and gratefully' (8 September 1935).

The *Jersey Leader* (13 September 1935) designated Barker the island's 'best publicity man. He has brought more famous people here than anyone else.' The paper noted the recent visit of Jack Petersen, the boxing champion, sent to Barker by Dr Biddle, of Cardiff, with a wrist injury, which Barker cured.

Elizabeth Arden, of cosmetics fame, was another of his visitors, travelling to see him from her home in New York. 'Sir Herbert cured her of a hip complaint she had suffered from for 15 years. As a gift, she furnished a room in his house here at St Lawrence with antiques, fine pictures, china, and a costly snow leopard rug.'

Writing what was to be his last letter to Barker (3 December 1935), from Burwash, Kipling proposed trying to interest Samuel Courtauld in endowing university chairs of manipulative surgery. He envied Barker's life in the more or less assured sunshine of Malaga—'lucky you'. The Burwash winter was vile, as usual. 'The wife' was not very well again. She was having more rheumatism that winter than before.

He had recently taken to the typewriter. 'Own typing on new machine', he wrote at the top of the letter to Barker. The impression given is not so much of a learner's fumbling effort as of enfeebled concentration. He typed 'waishe' for 'wishes', 'isalnd' for 'island', and showed ineptness in the use of the spacebar. He died six weeks later, two days before his friend King George V.

*

The memorably reiterated bulletin which informed the listening millions in the King's last hours that his life was 'moving peacefully towards its close', was drafted by Lord Dawson of Penn. Harley Street never soared more majestically in the realm of felicitous expression. Medical men of all degrees wrote to Dawson with pride in the part that he had taken in the nation's counsels at that time.

Consultants foregathering in those weeks recalled the story told by Graham-Hodgson, the radiologist in the medical team attending the King during his illness six years before. When he took his cumbersome portable apparatus to the Palace, he apologised for it to the King, and jocularly hoped that it would not set the room on fire. 'A bloody good thing if it does,' the King had retorted. 'My fire brigade haven't had anything to do for years.'

In the list of royal medical appointments, the name of Wilfred Trotter, MD, MS, FRCS, FRS, of 101 Harley Street, had not been conspicuous since that time. He had been brought in by Dawson to assist at the operation for pleural abscess that, with superb nursing, prolonged the King's life. Having then been made Serjeant-Surgeon to the King, a pinnacle of professional success, he now renounced private practice because it hindered his surgical research and teaching at University College Hospital. The annals of medicine show few comparable gestures. 'Money would not tempt him,' said Sir James Purves-Stewart. 'I failed to lure him from the walls of his hospital to see a case of brain tumour in a millionaire.'

Trotter's father was a West Country carpenter of the old breed whose handclasp was the sign-manual of the honest craftsman, and who gave the best that was in him to every task. His son, whose surgery was the admiration of his colleagues, used to say that his hands were clumsy by comparison with his father's. When the Gloucester carpenter moved to Willesden Green, the son quickly took advantage of the opportunities available in the metropolis for extended study, though at first it was feared that his constitution would not be equal to the demands of city life. He had long periods of invalidism, and a hint of frailty, accentuated by a slight stoop, went with him down the years, suiting the impression he gave of a pessimistic philosopher in an alien milieu. Recalling 'enlightening communions with Trotter', a colleague confessed that 'a short walk with him of some two hundred yards caused me to go and reconsider all my views on the teaching of surgery'. When, in 1914, Bertrand Russell announced that he 'proposed to dispense with his social instincts for the duration of the war, Trotter sardonically commented: "He might as well talk of dispensing with the nitrogen in his bones".'[1]

In breadth and power of thought, and in general culture, Wilfred Trotter was a superior being in the highest ranks of his profession. The mental aristocrat who wrote the classic

[1] Ernest Jones, MD: *Free Associations*, 1959.

Instincts of the Herd in Peace and War gained the affection as well as the respect of his contemporaries.

*

The London Clinic was in difficulties after only six years' existence, its affairs complicated by unforeseen costs that could not be recovered from patients hit by the economic crisis of 1931 and after. Out of the Georgian context of Upper Harley Street, its red brick storeys rose uncompromisingly above the tops of the plane trees of the Marylebone Road. Conceived by a group of local physicians and surgeons as the most advanced medical centre of its kind in England, it combined high class consultancy with the best possible therapeutic and nursing home facilities. In 1935, the Clinic was reorganised under a trust deed, when its administration was taken over and conducted on a non-profit basis by a sympathetic property developer, Aynsley Bridgland (later knighted). Among its amenities it provided consulting-rooms, with a common entrance at 149 Harley Street, for thirty specialists, who took long leases at rents that had to be drastically revised when reorganisation came.

Choosing the site, the London Clinic's original promoters obviously traded on the propinquity and prestige of Harley Street, which, it was hoped, would keep its five operating theatres fully occupied, its 180 expensive beds filled. In return, Harley Street profited by the immanence of the Clinic, with its aura of a medical Claridge's attracting the world's wealthy invalids. There was probably no medical or surgical problem that remained outside the scope of the Clinic's consultant services, which were augmented by two or three experienced general practitioners for the comfort of patients who still cherished the family doctor tradition.

The Clinic acquired a certain glamour from the patronage of royalty, stage and film personalities, and other fine-feathered patients. The ensuing publicity went against the Harley Street grain, and attempts were made to check excesses of advertisement without imperilling the waiting list. The eminence of some of the specialists who daily foregathered in their gloomy basement mess for lunch and smoking-room stories over the port ensured that the reputation of the Clinic as a fount of medical and surgical wisdom survived unimpaired.

A novel of mediocre literary merit, *The Citadel*, by A. J. Cronin, was widely in demand at the libraries in those middle-thirties. Reviewers picked it out, and editors gave it headlines, because of its exposure of Harley Street fee splitting and other deprecated practices. Readers rejoiced in the public discomfiture of what they regarded as a condescending professional class. A contributor to *The Lancet* wrote that 'the joy with which attacks like *The Citadel* are greeted is a measure of our popularity', and took consolation in the thought that 'we are certainly less unpopular than the Law'.

X

WAS IT A £50,000 SWINDLE?

'The ease with which the medical profession can be bamboozled' was the theme of a confidential memorandum written just before the Second World War by a doctor practising in the Harley Street precincts. A London financial house had been tipped off by a member of an equally reputable firm of international art dealers that Buda-Pest doctors had great expectations from a locally invented electro-physical aid to the detection of early cancer and other basic diseases. Its ultra-sensitivity allegedly enabled it to pick up the most minute electrical discharges from the body and to discriminate between normal and abnormal physical states. It was understood to have had the endorsement of the famous French scientist, Madame Joliot-Curie.

City information was that the inventor, described as an Hungarian electronics engineer, was negotiating a sale of his rights on monopoly terms to the Italian government. Quick action was necessary, as the inventor was said to be already in Bolzano, where he was meeting two Italians acting as agents for their government. The negotiations were likely to be concluded in a few days.

The London financiers arranged a guarantee of £50,000 from a well-known industrialist, who, 'in the name of humanity' hoped to divert the invention into the domain of British medical research, and eventually to make it available to the nation's hospitals. With that backing, the art dealer persuaded the inventor to suspend the Italian negotiations *pro tem*. Meanwhile, the financiers in London arranged for a British medical physicist of professorial standing to go out to Bolzano to meet the inventor. If the emissary from London thought well of the invention, he was empowered to secure an option at £50,000 on condition that the inventor brought his machine to England and submitted it to approved tests. He was to be offered liberal expenses and facilities.

The financial group engaged the services of a London doctor with specialist experience of the medical uses of electricity. He had 'vetted' several such devices, pronouncing more than ninety per cent of them worthless if not fraudulent. He fairly confidently expected the physicist to return inside a week with news of a wild goose chase. He had expressed in writing his view that 'the chance of its turning out to be genuine is not very great'.

He was surprised rather than gratified to receive, instead, a telegram from Italy intimating provisional approval of the machine, asking for 90,000 Swiss francs as an advance payment to the inventor, and for arrangements to be made for the latter to come to London for demonstrations. So it was that on a spring afternoon a small unofficial reception committee assembled at Croydon airport to meet the Paris plane. The group consisted of the doctor representing the City men, one of their legal advisers, and the art dealer who had introduced the project. In the words of the doctor, they were 'somewhat tense and excited' as they waited.

Secrecy was the watchword. Care had been taken to ensure that nothing reached the press. Unknown to the doctor, and considerably surprising him, passport and Customs formalities had been waived. The Hungarian inventor, accompanied by his British escort and an Austrian baroness to whom, it was understood, he had entrusted the business part of his mission, with three of his machines, was driven off to a London hotel. It was conveniently near the medical physicist's hospital. The inventor's life had been insured for £55,000. 'Are we mad?' the doctor wrote privately to a member of the City group for whom he was acting. 'Yes, quite, but it is amusing while it lasts.'

*

A demonstration was staged at the hospital. It was attended by about a dozen leaders of the medical profession, including Lord Dawson of Penn, President of the Royal College of Physicians. The selected cases, with the relevant notes, were segregated in an adjoining room. Care was taken to see that the inventor had no access to them. The organisers of the demonstration believed it to be foolproof. Not that the eminent consultants showed much interest. They sauntered about the room looking abstracted and bored. Some of them did not hide their suspicion that this was another Abrams Box affair.

The Hungarian inventor, holding a small instrument like a fountain-pen with a flex running back to his machine on its stand, traversed the first patient's body with the instrument. When a tiny light began to flicker in the instrument that he was holding, he proceeded to concentrate on the area indicated. Having manipulated knobs and switches, he dismissed the patient and communicated his finding: 'Secondary deposit of cancer.' The patient's notes were called for, and with them an X-ray picture taken earlier that day. They showed that the machine or its inventor had diagnosed correctly.

In the next case, he pin-pointed a small area of the skull, pronouncing in bad German: 'Not cancer but tumour here.' The neuro-surgeon in charge of the patient was at once alerted. He called for the case notes. Even the most languid of the consultants was attentive as he explained that he had already decided to open the skull within an inch of the point indicated by the machine.

Each of the ten cases was accurately diagnosed. By the end of the demonstration the consultants were bending over the machine, trying to show intelligent interest in its working, though none had any knowledge of electronics. All put their signatures to a memorandum stating that 'the instrument we have seen used today as an aid to diagnosis has proved itself of sufficient interest and importance to call for further and careful, unhurried investigations'. It was observed that Lord Dawson of Penn, 'oozing urbanity and tact, was deeply impressed by the results'.

The medical physicist who had brought the inventor to London was elated. The doctor acting for the City group was cautiously hopeful, though far from convinced. He had served on the Horder Committee that reported on the Abrams Box. Better equipped than most medical men with knowledge of the existence of electrical emanations from the heart, brain, and nervous system, he believed (as he still does) that advances would be made in that field of research.

The baroness now pressed for the option to be taken up at the agreed figure of £50,000. 'What further proof could you all want?' The London art dealer supported that demand. After discussions, a further trial period was agreed on, the inventor to be paid £25 a week by the syndicate for living expenses, pending a decisive report. Accommodation for his machines was made available at the doctor's consulting-room near Harley Street. Each night the Hungarian locked them in a cupboard and pocketed the key. He had promised to produce diagrams of his circuits and to supply other essential information.

New test cases were brought to him from hospitals, clinics, and private practices. They consisted of patients suffering from diseases capable of precise diagnosis. The results that impressed the consultants at the first demonstration were repeated. When a queried 'grumbling appendix' case was brought in, the machine registered a tubercular focus, from which the inventor deduced 'very early phthisis'. Sputum tests and X-rays followed, but supplied no corroboration. The diagnosis was written off as a failure. Two weeks later the patient showed symptoms that called for further sputum tests and X-ray pictures. They gave a positive result.

*

So far, the tests had been conducted without the help of an interpreter. As they went on, the language difficulty increased, particularly in regard to technicalities. A Hungarian business man working in the London textile trade agreed to bridge the gap. He was described as 'completely trilingual, obviously straight, competent, electrically knowledgeable, a delightful companion'. He was sensitive to the possibility of any fellow countryman of his trying to 'pull a fast one' over the British medical profession. His arrival on the scene had the effect of quickening doubts about the inventor's claims.

Those doubts were given substance when the doctor met Madame Joliot-Curie, after she had lectured at the Wigmore Hall. Had she, he asked, heard of the Hungarian diagnostic machine with which her name had been linked? 'Never,' she answered. Had her laboratory, as was claimed, sold radio-active isotopes to the inventor or to anyone in Hungary? The same emphatic answer was given. To the question: What would you say about anyone who claimed to have bought salts of the lighter metals from your laboratory and to have made them permanently radioactive? Madame Joliot-Curie replied: 'I would say that he was a common swindler.'

The doctor left Wigmore Hall resolved to apply more stringent methods of investigation. Meanwhile, the Hungarian interpreter, having seen his first demonstration of the machine, confided in the doctor his belief that the light that flickered in the inventor's diagnostic instrument could not possibly be produced by current generated in a patient's body, and that there must be a hidden source of energy. He was astonished that the medical physicist had not made the point that the 'pea-lamp' used in taking preliminary soundings required more power than was available from body emanations. The doctor, too, confessed that it had not occurred to him.

At the interpreter's prompting, the inventor permitted examination of the electrical equipment inside the casing of the machines. No batteries or other source of power or light were found in them. The interpreter remained unconvinced. There was hostility between him and his compatriot, who still had not produced the promised circuit diagrams.

The machines were taken to Cambridge for a full-scale test in the laboratory of a distinguished scientist fully qualified in both medicine and physics. He made it clear to everyone that, having provided the facilities, he would concur in nothing short of the most exacting inquiry into the working and the practical value of the machines, if any. He listened with judicial impassiveness to the inventor's explanations, apparently unheeding the interpreter's wry asides.

Soon it was obvious that there would be no tests in Cambridge. After seemingly intensive scrutiny of each machine, the inventor declared them out of order, possibly damaged in transit, and that they could be recalibrated only in London, As the doctor wrote afterwards: 'The tension in the car on the return journey was acute'. He was struck by the fact that when the inventor came to put the machines away for the night he departed from his normal routine of merely locking them in the cupboard. Each machine was criss-crossed with tape, the knots secured by a massive blob of sealing-wax.

Later that evening, the doctor returned to his consulting-room, the interpreter accompanying him. The interpreter easily picked the cupboard lock. Then by the deft use of extremely fine pliers he took the hinges off the casing of one machine and removed the binding tape without disturbing the seal. With a current-measuring instrument he went over every part of the machine, repeating under his breath that 'there must be a battery somewhere'. He was all but giving up, baffled, when the instrument registered a considerable deflection. Concealed most artfully in the windings of what appeared to be an ordinary small transformer was a rechargeable cell. The tape was replaced intact, the box cover screwed back, the picked lock adjusted. The two men then went back to the doctor's private sitting-room to consider what should be done.

Discovering a fake was one thing, convincing others of it another. Having at their disposal £50,000 for taking up an option as soon as the inventor's claims were warranted, the City group would naturally require proof that the concealed cell implied fraud. They could cite the fact that the physics professor had thought it worth while to bring the inventor and his machine to London. They had before them the encouraging report of the first set of tests, and with it the eminent consultants' memorandum. Understandably, they could take the view that it was traditional for qualified men to disparage the claims of laymen.

Reporting formally on the Cambridge fiasco, the doctor advised that the option money should be withheld 'until my final report is complete. Apparently conclusive as were the ten tests at the hospital, they do not provide final proof of the validity of the inventor's claims.' In the new situation, the doctor's problem was complicated by the disclosure that the £50,000 had already been paid to the baroness on the strength of the hospital demonstration.

*

'The ease with which the medical profession can be bamboozled', the text of the final summing-up of an extraordinary affair in Harley Street annals, was matched by the readiness with which certain men of acumen and integrity in the City of London backed a scheme that, for all its humanitarian implications, called for rigorous examination on personal as well as on technical grounds. Who were those Central Europeans who conducted what was finally conceded by its victims to be an ingenious swindle? Not until three years later, when attempts were made to recover the £50,000, were inquires made into their backgrounds and standing. The baroness was 'entirely unknown in Hungary'. The inventor, who turned out to be a small manufacturer of sunlamps, was regarded as 'a poor risk' in his own business community, a man 'whose character is differently judged'.

In the *dramatis personae*, as the files show,[1] the name of the art dealer was prominent. He had been a familiar and respected figure in the London art market. The City men were apparently unaware that his personal affairs were in some disarray, and that he was facing bankruptcy proceedings. It was believed that he was in closer touch with the mysterious baroness than was realised in the beginning. So, it was thought,

[1] I was given access to the files on the understanding that the names of the principals should be withheld from any account that I might write of the events here recorded.—R.P.

were the two Italians who posed as agents for their government, and with whom the art dealer also was in contact. They showed fright on hearing that the London financiers were proposing to inform the Italian government of their activities concerning the invention.

Renewing his unhappy part in the transactions, the industrialist wrote at the end of 1938: 'I was an entire outsider. The only action I took was to express a strong warning against fraud—as exemplified by a previous experience, and escape, of mine in respect of an electrically applied non-corrosive paint offered to me.' As for his lost £50,000, 'I found the money in the earnest desire to benefit the world in its search for the cure and prevention of cancer.'

Earnest discussion produced the final decision that there should be no dramatic exposure of the inventor or his invention, so-called. Publicity might be unpleasant. Too many reputations were involved. The experts continued to be baffled by the inventor's spectacular initial success with the ten hospital cases. Did he understand English while all the time pretending not to? Had he made contacts at the hospital in advance? Was he gifted with extra-sensory perception? The only ascertainable answer was to the second question; and it was satisfactorily established that he had not been near the hospital before the first demonstration.

He and his machines were quietly returned to Hungary by air, after which the City men decided to 'call it a day'. It was afterwards learnt that the Swiss customs authorities had ordered the inventor off the plane and subjected him to a most thorough search before letting him proceed. They found a large magnet sewn into the lapel of his jacket. No information was forthcoming about its purpose.

The files closed with a London newspaper paragraph stating that in May 1940 the Baroness von X— had been sentenced to death in her absence by a Paris court. She was heard of again in 1948, when she was reported to have been tried by another court and acquitted. Those happenings imparted a new note of mystery into the case. Was the whole affair espionage cover?

The question was often asked later among those involved. If they found the answer, they did not commit it to the files.

*

The year 1936 was a climacteric one in the history of the long running battle between Barker 'the bonesetter', as he was still often called (to his annoyance), and medical orthodoxy. It opened with a confidential letter from Rowley Bristow, writing from 102 Harley Street as president of the British Orthopaedic Association, the membership of which included many distinguished surgeons. 'I am endeavouring to get the Association to invite you to demonstrate before them' (10 January).

Barker was gratified; perhaps not utterly surprised. He had been asked by Lord Moynihan to call on him at 11 Portland Place, W. Remembering that celebrated surgeon's harsh behaviour towards him in the presence of the Minister of Health seven years previously, he was naturally curious to know the reason for the invitation. Lord Moynihan explained that he had lately seen a spinal case that, after years of ineffectual orthodox treatment, had yielded to Barker's skill. Impressed, he wanted Barker to give a demonstration 'before leading members of the faculty'. Barker told him of the offers that he had made, and renewed, over the years, and of the total lack of response from the doctors. 'It shall be arranged,' Moynihan promised.

Afterwards, Barker learnt that Moynihan wrote that evening to the president of the British Orthopaedic Association. There were grounds for believing that, apart from Lord Moynihan's powerful interest, Barker's public dissociation of his work from that of the osteopaths, whose propaganda was vociferous, assisted the orthopaedic surgeons' change of heart.

Moynihan wrote to him on 5 March 1936: 'I returned only today from the East after a wonderful holiday.' He had voyaged from Singapore with 'a Mr Melita, who spoke in highly enthusiastic and most grateful terms of the immediate and immense help you had given him'. Moynihan went on to say that he had been in touch with Rowley Bristow about the proposed demonstration. 'There is still too much incredulity and far too much apathy.'

Barker was expecting Augustus John to stay with him in Malaga. 'Alas! As usual, I find myself stuck with work which for financial reasons I cannot neglect.' The artist had been spending money on alterations to his house at Fordingbridge, Hampshire, 'so that my available funds are more than usually low'. He hoped that there would be a later invitation. 'I somehow feel I would prove as good a subject for your art, as you for mine. I need all the years available to do what I have in view within my power,' and he had not 'the slightest doubt' that Barker 'could extend those years substantially'. He had recommended C. B. Cochran, the famous London stage producer, to consult Barker about his arthritic hip.

When newspapers announced that Barker was to demonstrate before the surgeons, H. G. Wells wrote to him from the Reform Club: 'I'm delighted to see that obdurate profession has at last taken you to its bosom. I shall hope to have a chance of seeing you when you come to London in July,' the month appointed for the demonstration. Wells asked him: 'What sort of place is Malaga for the winter? I've given up my place at Grasse,' and he wanted to hear of some sunny resort to which he could retreat when coughs and colds assailed him (21 May 1936). By June, Cochran was telling Barker in a letter written from Torremolinos: 'I arrived here a very broken man—you were my last hope. It is beyond me to express all I feel now. My gratitude to you is beyond such words as I can put together. Thank you and bless you' (2 June 1936).

Barker's demonstration was to be given at St Thomas's Hospital, London, on 22 July 1936. Moynihan wrote to him from Carr Manor, Meanwood, Leeds: 'I am rejoiced at your news.' Suggesting that Barker should avoid a possible 'constitutional difficulty' by indicating in advance what cases he would like to treat, rather than by going into the wards and picking them out on the day, as he was proposing to do, Moynihan added: 'What I want is a fair trial on cases which give you a chance of demonstrating methods perhaps unknown to, or inadequately practised, by our profession.' He forecast 'a spectacular success', and that 'many stubborn barriers' would be broken down. He would 'most certainly' be present at the demonstration, and looked forward to it 'with great hope' (3 June 1936).

That there were still points of resistance was made plain in a letter written to Barker by H. T. Fairbanks, FRCS, of 84 Harley Street, two days before the demonstration at St Thomas's, to which he was invited. He was brought up to believe, he wrote, that practitioners who had not been through the normal medical training were not to be encouraged. 'I still believe this to be true.' His friends had told him: 'This is an exceptional case.' He agreed, replying to them that he was 'sorely tempted', but that he could not ignore the principle involved. Attendance at the demonstration would be regarded 'as approval of unqualified practice in general', and he could not see that 'as a good thing'. Having received 'nothing but friendliness and courtesy' from Barker, he now had to do 'what must seem a scurvy trick', and decline the invitation.

*

'A sudden sense of my own isolation came upon me.' Barker was writing of his emotion at entering 'the amphitheatre of that great hospital beside the grey waters of the Thames'. He felt like the central figure 'in a State trial of manipulative surgery'. His arrival was awaited by an audience consisting of practically the entire membership of the British Orthopaedic Association, numbering over a hundred surgeons. Also present were Lord Moynihan, and present and past occupants of chairs of surgery at several universities.

Barker was introduced as a practitioner 'who has had a long and vast experience'. He had been invited to come before the meeting 'not to revive any of the old controversy, not in pursuit of any medico-political motive, but in a spirit of inquiry and in a search for knowledge'.

What he apparently did not realise, or subconsciously ignored, was that for many of the orthopaedic surgeons gathered that day at St Thomas's Hospital, manipulation was no longer 'a hinterland of surgery', as he had for so many years insisted. Orthopaedics had moved forward in line with other surgical advances made since the First World War, and manipulation was practised more widely within the medical profession than he knew. He was fighting a battle that had largely been won. What he had to demonstrate was not a series of new techniques but his own inimitable skill.

He was manifestly pleased by the welcome given him as he walked forward to begin the demonstration. His voice was muffled by a heavy throat cold, and he asked to be excused giving detailed explanations as he worked. He presented seventeen assorted orthopaedic cases, spinal injuries, recurrent shoulder dislocations (which the surgeons said could be cured only by open operation), knee cartilage derangements, displaced hips, tennis elbows (one, a doctor's), and other joint and tendon disabilities. The *British Medical Journal* noted 'the quiet confidence which the demonstrator had in his methods'. After successfully manipulating a shoulder 'that had dislocated countless times during 15 years' (*The Lancet*), Barker told the assembly: 'I don't quite know how I do this operation.'

He thought it 'a strange situation. Here am I, an outcast, demonstrating to some of the most famous orthopaedic surgeons in the world.' Never before had an unqualified man come before the medical faculty in England. Thanking the anaesthetist for his services, and thinking of his old friend Axham, he said that he 'could not resist' remarking to the surgeons nearest to him: 'Gentlemen, are you not guilty now of infamous conduct?' None the less, he felt at the end of the demonstration that 'the atmosphere was happy and appreciative'.

Rowley Bristow assured him that 'the demonstration was a great success'. *The Times* thought 'the occasion a matter of congratulation, not only because it brings a long controversy to an end, but also because knowledge, recognized as special in point of scope and value, has been freely offered and gladly received by those in a position to use it and transmit it to others ... Public opinion will endorse a step which is in the highest traditions of surgical practice in this country, and will join with those who came to the demonstration in thanking Sir Herbert Barker' (23 July 1936).

At Oxford, where the scientific sections of the British Medical Association were meeting that same week, A. S. Blundell Bankart, FRCS, told his audience how Barker had cured a patient of his foot trouble for which he himself had treated her unsuccessfully for the past two years. The Warden of New College, H. A. L. Fisher, wrote to Barker: 'I was very glad to see the prominence given in *The Times* to your notable demonstration which was, I hope, as successful as you were confident that it would be. As you will have noted, the matter has been engaging the attention of the BMA here' (24 July 1936). The Warden's letter was followed by one from The Provost of Worcester College and Vice-Chancellor of the University (1932–5), the Rev. F. J. Lys. 'Mr H. A. L. Fisher has just been telling me of his debt to you. I gather that you discovered and put right a displacement or disorder of his spine of which the doctors had no suspicion, and have put him on the way to complete recovery.' The Provost reported: 'I have a sound knee, owing to your manipulation of it in 1911.' As a sufferer from an undiagnosed back pain, for which he had fruitlessly consulted medical specialists, he now hoped that Barker would see him again.

There was remembrance from Murray Brumwell, the retired assistant editor of *The Times*. 'I never doubted your success if you were given a chance to demonstrate your work, but what a strain after all these weary years of waiting for proper recognition! If the doctors who copy you do not attain full success, that can hardly be expected. Much of your gift is personal. Bankart's was a valuable confession.' Brumwell had heard from Webb, his late secretary at *The Times*, a patient of Barker's. 'He and I will never forget what you have done for one who was losing faith in his future happiness' (27 July

1936). Barker had recently treated Seymour Hicks, the actor-manager, 'enabling him to kneel to receive his knighthood'.

Arbuthnot Lane wrote to Barker: 'I heard all about your demonstration and was very pleased that you had been given such an excellent reception. You have fully justified your existence.' Lane was distressed by the unexpected death, two weeks before, of Lord Moynihan. 'It seems to me strange that men like Moynihan, who have dealt with abdominal conditions for so long, have no knowledge of the laws of health.' There was a postscript to Lane's letter. 'The mills of God grind slowly, but they grind very fine. It takes a long time to impress truth upon the public' (15 September 1936).

A thrustful newcomer to Harley Street, Archibald McIndoe, who, after a thin time as a would-be specialist in abdominal surgery, was being compassionately employed as assistant by Sir Harold Gillies, by then world renowned as a plastic surgeon, wrote to ask Barker if he would treat 'young Fairey, son of the aircraft manufacturer'. The case was one of severe back injury incurred at football. The young man had been seen by five qualified orthopaedic specialists. He showed no improvement. In a little more than a month, his father, Sir Richard Fairey, was writing to Barker to express 'sincere gratitude for the literally miraculous result'. Endorsing that verdict, McIndoe told Barker: 'It is indeed a sort of miracle.'

It was as if the inexplicable, or, as some thought, occult element in Barker's gift developed to a climax in those years. Bristow, who was preparing a report on the demonstration at St Thomas's, wrote to him: 'It is not easy, I find, to assess the causes of your success correctly and to exclude the psychical side. I am clear in my own mind that it plays a greater part than you are inclined to believe' (18 September 1936). Like a painter or a composer, he did not know how he produced his best results.

The Duke of Kent was 'deprived of the one great pleasure of his private life, playing the piano', by the almost complete contraction of the little finger of his right hand, ascribed to a faulty surgical operation done by a Royal Navy surgeon six years before. Barker was consulted on behalf of the duke by his friend Lord Tredegar (Evan Morgan), who apologised for intruding on his retirement, at the same time hoping that he would 'consent to wait upon His Royal Highness', at Belgrave Square, and perhaps 'bring back to this young man the joy of once more being able to play the piano'. The defective finger was also a hindrance to the duke's public handshaking. Barker put it right in three visits—'simply magnificent', wrote McIndoe, who took charge of the case when Barker was called away from London.

*

Barker awaited with some anxiety the report on his demonstration at St Thomas's. When he wrote to Bristow, inquiring when it would be ready, he received the reply: 'It must not be hurried because every word wants carefully weighing.' Bristow regarded it as 'a very great responsibility'. Barker's pioneer work 'should have and shall have, full acknowledgment', but it would be wrong to suggest, Bristow reminded him, that the medical profession still failed to realise the value of manipulative methods.[1]

Barker returned to London on 26 February 1937, when Shaw and Wells were his guests at lunch at the Dorchester Hotel. The following day, *The Lancet* published *Case Reports and Notes* on the demonstration, contributed by W. Rowley Bristow, FRCS. He recorded a series of striking results, followed up some months after manipulation by Barker. 'Astonishingly good', *The Times* commented. Bristow observed in the *Notes* that 'Barker possesses a very strong personality. Once he undertakes the treatment of a patient, he does not visualise the possibility of failure. This tremendous optimism must have and does have its effect upon the patient.'

Having set out in his report the results in each of the cases that Barker had dealt with at St Thomas's, Bristow appended

---

[1] A. G. Timbrell Fisher, FRCS, was the author of *Treatment by Manipulation*, and James Mennell, MD was writing his subsequently published textbook, *The Science and Art of Joint Manipulation*.

a 'critical survey' of the demonstration. Its conclusion was a triumphant vindication of all that Barker had striven for through thirty years. 'It is due to Barker to say that but for his pioneer work the manipulative field of orthopaedic surgery would not occupy the position it does today, and that had his offers to demonstrate his technique been accepted twenty-five years ago the general utilisation of this branch of therapeutics would not have been so long delayed.'

The newspapers made the report an event of that week in February 1937. 'A landmark in surgical history', said *The Observer*. 'A chapter is concluded in which the outstanding honours belong to Sir Herbert himself and those medical men who assisted him for the sake of humanity at the cost of professional ostracism.' A leading article in *The Times* praised both Barker and the medical profession.

Letters and messages reached Barker from all quarters. His wife, Jean, staying with him at the Hans Crescent Hotel, S.W. could not forbear joining in the congratulatory flow. *With joy I send loving greetings to my Boneo on this day of triumph as we have shared the long controversy together I know how much it means to you.*

Heavily and often unfairly weighted against the medical profession, the newspaper publicity drew comments on Barker's work from orthopaedic surgeons in subsequent issues of *The Lancet*. They were concerned to make it clear that certain of his methods were already standard practice in their branch of surgery. Blundell Bankart questioned the validity of Barker's treatment of the recurrent shoulder dislocation that was one of the more spectacular cases presented at St Thomas's. Barker took exception to his comments in *The Lancet*. Replying privately to him, Bankart wrote from 95 Harley Street: 'Is it too late for you to realise that you are no longer "up against it", and that every man's hand is not turned against you? You must have known that the last thing I wanted was to have a jab at you' (15 March 1937).

What Bankart and his colleagues in orthopaedic surgery did not explain was why, apart from his seemingly mysterious

Left : Lord Evans. 'His personal style was that of a conformist serving the established order with distinguished efficiency.' *Below :* 'Tommy' Horder preparing to address one of the early meetings of his Fellowship for Freedom in Medicine.

92 Harley Street. Disraeli's criticism of Harley Street as 'flat, spiritless, and dull', is belied by the surviving Georgian grace of many of the interiors.

83 Harley Street. 'So many patients would poke the waiting-room fire to relieve their feelings. This led to dust and ashes being scattered in all directions.' (*Dr. Byam in Harley Street, 1962*.)

power, Barker continued to receive so many of their failures. One of the latest of them, C. E. M. Joad, the popular philosopher and broadcaster, had written to him only a few days before: 'I feel under such a debt of obligation to you that I have lain awake at night wondering how to repay it' (7 March 1937). 'Forget the scars and think of the victory', was the advice given to Barker by Sir John Weir, MD, Physician-in-Ordinary to the new King, Edward VIII (13 March 1937). 'To nobody does the recognition which you have won bring greater pleasure than to Yours sincerely, Archibald Sinclair.' That future Minister of the Crown added his opinion that, 'quite frankly, the restoration of Dr Axham's name to the Register seems to me a very small thing compared with the honour which is now attributed to his name as an undaunted associate of yours' (24 March 1937).

*

The age of florid medical affluence was passing. One of its last and by no means forlorn survivors was Sir Stanley Woodwark, KCMG, CBE, JP, DL, MD, FRCP, MRCS, FRSM, FZS, who had a lucrative general practice, with valuable insurance connections, at 6 Harley Street, and who carried himself with an air of almost sublime self-sufficiency. He was one of those men to be found in all the professions who, not being naturally endowed with the rare quality called presence, have no compunction in simulating it. The Regency buck façade of full morning dress, with dove-grey waistcoat, striped silk stock, pink carnation, white spats, embellished no outstanding attainment in clinical medicine, though he was a fine administrator. His gifts, apart from a generous flair for good fellowship, might have been successfully displayed in the forensic arena. Talk was one of his life's enjoyments, heightened by his readiness to hear what he himself had to say, probably less from vanity than for the pleasure of exercising a fastidiously cultivated fluency. As one of the more popular members of the Savage Club, he was the unacknowledged model for character drawings by the famous *Punch* artists, George Belcher and

G. L. Stampa, It was another in that witty company who suggested when Woodwark mentioned that he had bought a house in Kent and was thinking of changing its name: 'Why not call it Bedside Manor?'

His elegant deportment contrasted with a naïveté not uncommon among men of exclusive interests and training. It was revealed one night when Basil Cameron, orchestra conductor, Sir Arnold Bax, composer, Philip Page, music critic, and the present writer, fell into a desultory discussion of the homosexual bias of James Agate, the dramatic and literary critic, who had just left the dinner table. Sir Stanley Woodwark had been reclining, apparently asleep, in a nearby armchair. Presently, he rose to his dominating height and, addressing the group, said: 'Forgive me, you fellows, if I seem to be butting in. I couldn't help overhearing your conversation. As a Harley Street man, with forty years' fairly intimate experience of human nature, I want to say—if you will allow me—that I've never come across a case of the kind you've been talking about, I've never met any other medical man who has, and I don't believe for one moment that such a thing exists outside your rather morbid imaginations. Good night.'

XI

SPEECH THERAPY FOR THE KING

The accession of George VI in December 1936 was possibly of more resounding significance for one of Harley Street's few non-medical practitioners than for the Physicians-in-Ordinary and Surgeons Extraordinary attached to the Court. Lionel Logue, the Australian speech therapist, had imparted to the new monarch, as Duke of York, a measure of self-confidence that had been sought in vain from other counsellors, among them his doctors and nine speech specialists.

For ten years, Logue had been helping the Duke to overcome the stammer that was the bane of his public life. In 1926, the Duke was preparing to go on a Commonwealth tour, dreading the inevitable round of speechmaking. His inability to conquer unaided a defect that had handicapped him from the age of six was a cause of much private distress. Even to propose 'the King' in a Royal Navy wardroom was a torment to him because of his fear of the 'k' sound. Increasingly, he tended to avoid meeting strangers lest he be tongue-tied. He was never sure of being able to sustain a conversation beyond a few halting phrases. His wife's devoted watchfulness averted many social embarrassments.

Lionel Logue, then forty-six, came from Burnside, South Australia, the son of a vintner. After college at Adelaide, he went to work with an electrical engineering firm engaged in installing the first supply of electricity at the Kalgoorlie goldmines. With the completion of the contract, he had enough money to enable him to relax for a few months while he contemplated his next step in life. It was natural that as a young man he should gravitate to the nearest city, which was Perth.

One of Logue's personal assets was a pleasant speaking voice. He joined the North Perth Choral Society, and contributed recitations from Shakespeare and Dickens to its programmes. In 1908, he started his own elocution school in Perth, and founded the city's Public Speaking Club. His was the voice chosen to provide the verbal accompaniment of a coronation programme, entitled *Royal England*, presented at Perth in August 1911. It consisted of a showing of 'animated pictures specially cinematographed by C. Spencer from privileged positions along the route'.

> Sailor George today's our ruler! Bless his honest kindly heart!
> Working hard to serve his country, and to play a kingly part.
> Not for him the joy of battle, knightly prowess—warrior's
>   fame—
> Kings no longer join in combat, but they serve us just the same;
> In the quiet work of kingship—daily task and common thing.
> And we cheer a fellow worker, when we shout *God Save the King!*

Declaiming those impassioned banalities from the wings of the New Theatre Royal, Perth, Lionel Logue would have been mightily astonished could he have divined that a King of England would one day seek his help as an authority on speech difficulties. His understanding of them was deepened when, after being medically rejected for Army service in the First World War, he worked on an Australian welfare committee dealing with returned soldiers. Some were handicapped by speech defects resulting from traumatic war experiences. His success in 'doctoring voices', particularly those of young patients, gained him a considerable reputation in South Australia.

Some time in 1923, a member of the entourage of the State Governor remarked to Logue's wife, apropos the forthcoming royal visit, that 'the Duke of York could do with your husband's help'. Presumably not on the basis of that casual comment, Logue sailed for England with his wife and three sons on 1 March 1924. Not an assertively ambitious man, he was thinking about the future of his sons. He was richer in experience than in capital. His personality, embellished by notably blue eyes and a good head of hair (which he cherished to the extent of regularly consulting a trichologist), made a favourable impression wherever he went. His self-training in elocution had purged his speech of all but the faintest trace of his Antipodean origin.

In London, he rented a second-floor room at 146 Harley Street, redecorated it in smoke-grey and pale blue, and was soon in practice as a speech therapist, his first patients sent to him by Australians living in London. It was the year of the British Empire Exhibition at Wembley. He took his son Laurie there on the last day. The Duke of York performed the closing ceremony. Hearing him speak, noting his hesitancies, Logue remarked to his son as the cheering died away: 'He's too old for me to manage a complete cure. But I could very nearly do it. I'm sure of that.'

*

The Duke showed impatience when Logue's name was first mentioned to him by a member of his staff. 'He had had his fill of specialists who claimed to be able to cure stammering and he was thoroughly discouraged by a series of failures.'[1] The Duchess of York had some difficulty in persuading him to see Logue, who subsequently wrote in his private notes:

'On October 19, 1926, the Duke of York entered my consulting-room at 3 in the afternoon, a slim, quiet young man with tired eyes, and all the outward signs of one upon whom habitual speech defect had begun to set its mark.' Retracing the patient's case history, Logue discovered that one of his focal memories was of a day when, as an Osborne cadet, the boy Prince Albert (as he was then) was 'struck dumb' by a question peremptorily put to him by a tutor who was unaware of his speech impediment: What is the half of one-half? The boy could have answered as promptly as any other but for his

[1] *King George VI: His Life and Reign*, by J. W. Wheeler-Bennett (Macmillan, 1958).

fear of uttering the word 'quarter'. Logue found that a similar fear overcame him when he had to say 'King' or 'Queen'. As often as was feasible, he used the formula, 'Their Majesties'.

As in many of his cases, Logue found that faulty breathing was a source of difficulty. He required his patients to apply his instructions in 'an hour's concentrated effort every day'. They were to practise daily breathing exercises devised by him, gargle regularly with warm water, and stand by an open window intoning the vowels 'in a fairly loud voice', each sound to last fifteen seconds. Given that degree of co-operation, he promised improvement if not final cure.

In the case of the Duke of York, he insisted that his consultations with the patient should take place 'in new surroundings', by which he meant 146 Harley Street, or his small flat in The Boltons, South Kensington. He further stipulated that they must meet 'on equal terms', regarding a free-and-easy personal relationship as an important part of the treatment. 'When he left at 5 o'clock', Logue wrote, rounding off his notes of the visit, 'one could see that there was hope once more in his heart.' Logue had revived it by his quiet penetrating optimism, and by a man-to-man approach that for the patient was no doubt a new and refreshing experience.

It was Queen Mary's wish that Logue should be appointed to the Duke's staff for the Commonwealth tour. Logue pointed out that self-reliance was an essential element in the case, and asked to be excused. Persuasion was brought to bear on him. He remained firm in his view that it would be 'a psychological error', and the project was dropped.

Within two months, the Duke was writing to Logue from 17 Bruton Street, W.: 'I must send you a line to tell you how grateful I am for all you have done in helping me with my speech defect. I really do think you have given me a good start in the way of getting over it. I am full of confidence for my coming trip, anyhow. Again, very many thanks' (5 January 1927).

The Duke repeated his appreciation in a letter written on board H.M.S. *Renown* at Panama: 'Your teaching, I must say, has given me a tremendous amount of confidence. You remember my fear of "The King". I give it every evening at dinner on board. This does not worry me any more' (25 January 1927). Later in the tour, at Sydney, he wrote: 'I have ever so much more confidence in myself and don't brood over a speech as in the old days. I know what to do now and the knowledge has helped me over and over again' (26 March 1927).

Five days after his return to London in June 1927, the Duke resumed his regular visits to Logue in Harley Street. Later that year, he wrote to tell Logue that he had 'talked a lot with the King', his father, and expressed his relief at 'not having to repeat everything over again', as formerly. Lord Dawson of Penn, visiting Balmoral at the same time, 'noticed the difference' in the Duke's speech, whereupon the Duke told him of the treatment he was having and suggested to Dawson that he should send his stammering cases to Logue, 'and to no one else ! ! !'

The regular consultations, interrupted only by the Duke's public and family duties, brought the two men, so far apart in station, into an accord reached by few with far more impressive qualifications who were in attendance at Court. Logue's frank, straightforward style, devoid of needless punctilio, was doubtless an added commendation to the Duke. They laughed together over the tongue-twisters prescribed by Logue as part of his treatment. 'Let's go gathering heathy heather with the gay brigade of grand dragoons' was varied by 'She sifted seven thick-stalked thistles through a strong thick sieve', and so on. Their letter exchanges, and Logue's notes, suggest that the Duke found much pleasure in the friendly understanding that developed between them. He wrote from Glamis Castle on 5 September 1930 to tell Logue, after the birth of Princess Margaret: 'We had a long time to wait but everything went off successfully. My youngest daughter has a fine pair of lungs. The waiting did not affect my speech at all.'

Writing to the Duke, and, later, when His Royal Highness ascended the Throne, Logue used the second-person pronoun with a freedom that would have offended the susceptibilities of sticklers for Court etiquette. Unlike the medical members of the Royal Household, he was not appointed 'to have, hold, exercise, and enjoy the said Place, together with all Rights, Profits, Privileges and Advantages thereunto belonging'. Logue's status at Court was always unofficial. He never took advantage of it for self-advertisement.

The Duke's readiness to make the most of Logue's teaching was such that he missed none of their appointments during the first two years of the treatment. Logue's notes show how much of its success was due to the Duke's own determination to obey the rules laid down for him. He continued to have qualms about speaking in public, 'but nothing happens actually during a speech to make me worry any more', he wrote on 22 September 1932. He still spoke slowly and deliberately, but with fewer hesitations. In cases such as his, Logue advised the patient to stop pausing between individual words, and to pause, instead, between groups of words.

Commenting on the Duke of York's public appearances in 1934, a newspaper writer observed that 'his pauses used to be disturbing. Now they add solemnity to great occasions.' When a woman columnist wrote: 'How well the Duke of York has trained himself to speak—thanks largely to Sir Louis Greig' (the Duke's comptroller), Logue underlined the paragraph heavily and perhaps sardonically. Sir Louis, who had been a Royal Navy surgeon, believed that the original cause of the Duke's speech trouble was his father's impatience with his left-handedness as a boy.

Logue was perhaps unduly, if naturally, sensitive to all public references to the Duke's vocal disability. He feared that they might have adverse psychological effects. He was exasperated when the Archbishop of Canterbury, Dr Lang, made mention of it in his Abdication broadcast of 13 December 1936, two days after the Duke's accession to the Throne as King George VI. 'When his people listen to him, they will note an occasional and momentary hesitation in his speech'.

Logue's dismay was great. For him, that nation-wide

emphasis on the defect that he had done so much to remedy was potent with disaster, jeopardising his painstaking labours of the previous ten years. The Archbishop had clearly not considered the possible consequences of his remarks at that time of unprecedented emotional stress for the King.

All fears, Logue's included, were removed when at Windsor, on 23 April 1937, the King unveiled the memorial to his late father, and made his first speech as the new monarch. It was an occasion on which he might well have faltered. Logue's satisfaction in his patient's performance was heightened by the remark he overheard as he watched the ceremony: 'But I thought the King had a speech impediment—the Archbishop said so!'

Through the first five months of that year, leading up to the Coronation on 12 May, Logue had a series of meetings with the King; no longer at Harley Street, but at Buckingham Palace and Windsor Castle. The Coronation was a more severe test for George VI than for most of his regal predecessors. The Oath, with its altered phrasing, reflecting constitutional changes, was rehearsed repeatedly with Logue. He was given a particular place in the Abbey on Coronation Day. The King was more than once seen to glance towards him. At the end of the great day, Logue was received by the Queen, who thanked him for his services.

He was summoned again to help with the King's first Christmas broadcast that year. Listening at home to its delivery, he wrote: 'If he had stammered as badly as of old, he would have taken not a quarter of an hour but 2 hrs. 28 mins'.

*

On 4 May 1939, the eve of the departure of the King and Queen for Canada and the United States, Logue was at Buckingham Palace to discuss the broadcasts and speeches confronting the King during an unusually strenuous tour. 'Saw Lascelles [Sir Alan Lascelles, the King's private secretary], he wrote, 'and told him what to do with the King before broadcasts. The height of the microphone, and the fact that the King likes to stand when broadcasting, not, as the Press always portray him, sitting down. At 5.30 the message came down: "Mr Logue wanted", and I was shown into the presence. He looked tired, and *was* tired—too tired to stand up and go through the speeches, but he had his smile and was quite happy. We did the Quebec speech and had just started on the Unveiling the Memorial speech when the hidden door in the wall opened and in came the Queen and the two Princesses. I bowed over the Queen's hand. She looked marvellous in brown, with her lovely blue eyes.'

He noted that the two princesses 'crowded round the King and begged, as it was their last night, that they could stay up late and go into the swimming pool. "Oh, do, Daddy—do, Daddy! It's our last night", at which the King gave in—and who would not?' They were allowed to go into the pool 'provided they were out of it by 6.30'. The King then bade Logue: 'Tell them about the time you dived on to the shark,' and Logue dutifully related an experience that befell him while he was swimming at Brighton, South Australia, when he was ten years old. 'As I told the story, the two princesses, their eyes wide open and their hands clasped, gazed up at me enthralled. I then shook hands with the Queen and wished her a good trip and a safe return, and as she went through the door with her lovely smile she turned and said: "We're looking forward to coming home already!"'

Logue added to his notes on that occasion: 'We rehearsed the speeches again and the King did them splendidly'. When he wished the King 'all sorts of good luck' on the coming journey, His Majesty replied: 'Many thanks, Logue, for all your trouble. I am very lucky to have a man who understands voices and speech so well.'

Logue's success at that high altitude was proof that speech therapy represented another deplorable gap in medical teaching. About thirty years earlier, the Rev. A. J. Church recalled in his *Memories of Men and Books* that as a boy of fourteen he was operated on by James Yearsley, MD, of 15 Savile Row, the first medical man to practise as an ear, nose and throat special-ist. 'He professed to cure stammering by cutting away the tonsils and uvula.' The patient in the case put it on record: 'I do not think that the treatment did me any good.'

In 1922, H. St John Rumsey, MA, like Logue, a lay therapist, had provided *The Lancet* with a series of papers on speech defects. Few of Logue's Harley Street neighbours were com-petent to advise his sort of patient, and fewer still had any insight into the tensions and distresses that brought them to him. Logue soon arrived at doyen status among the relatively small number of practitioners of his speciality. As a founder of the British Society of Speech Therapists, he projected his teaching and influence well beyond his length of days.

His casenotes indicated that in some instances paternal tyranny was a likely cause of stammering. The wealthy head of an international commodity business consulted him about his son, whose halting speech was seriously hindering his pro-gress at Harrow School. He asked Logue how long the neces-sary treatment would take, and what would be the fee. Logue told him: 'It will take twelve months, and my fee would be a thousand pounds.' On the following day, he received by post a cheque for £500, with a request that he would begin the treatment as soon as possible. Logue returned the cheque, reiterating that his fee for the case would be £1,000. 'The fees of the rich', he wrote to the father of the boy, 'enable me to treat many poor patients for nothing.' Some time later, the son telephoned to Logue, 'in a terrible state of mind. His father refused to help him. The boy implored me to see him.' He did so, and subsequently treated the boy successfully and without charge.

Another of his cases was the badly afflicted son of a well-known shipowner, whom it amused to make fun of the young man's hampered speech at board meetings. The son consulted Logue privately. Logue liked telling the story of 'the old man's amazement' on the day that his son addressed the board 'with-out a speech flaw of any kind'.

*

Unknown to them, the orthopaedic surgeons earned a compliment from Shaw when in 1939 they unanimously accepted Barker's offer to teach his manipulative methods at St Thomas's Hospital 'to those who care to acquire it'. Shaw told Barker in a letter that it was 'astonishingly enlightened' of St Thomas's to do at last what all the medical schools should have done long before. He advised Barker not to antagonise the osteopaths. Pointing out what he considered to be serious defects in their teaching and practice, he suggested that in time they would be glad to add Barker's technique 'to their repertory' (11 March 1939).

Later in the year, it was announced that Barker's work was to be perpetuated on film, to be made in the orthopaedic department at St Thomas's. It would provide a permanent record of his teachings. In that form, they would be available to future generations of students. 'He is delighted by this full measure of recognition of the value of his work,' *The Times* stated in a long review of his career (27 July 1939). Barker responded with the comment: 'My labours have not been in vain. The battle for manipulative surgery is won.'

By no means in the grip of the *Nunc Dimittis* mood, gratified by the goodwill of the orthopaedic surgeons, he still hankered after more formal recognition. He raised again the question of his receiving a Lambeth medical degree, entitling him to the satisfaction of writing MD after his name, though as a decoration, not a qualification. Archbishop Davidson had given a good reason for not granting it. Archbishop Lang, nearly twenty years after, might find a better reason for reversing that decision. Barker wrote twice to his friend, Basil Peto, MP, asking him to support a new application. It was not proceeded with because of the war, which also precluded Barker from carrying out his teaching programme at St Thomas's.

Still not taking his retirement seriously, his friends, acquaintances, and admirers continued to trespass on it. Augustus John, 'in need of tuning up again', wondered if Barker was coming to London and, if so, when. 'I want a good 20 years to do something respectable.' Others, like John, had come to look on Barker as a *magus* who held the key to a ripe old age. Sir John Lavery, RA, at seventy-two, recovering from 'a loathsome disease that Horder called bronchial pneumonia', wrote to ask: 'I wonder if your opinion of my years still holds good. Dr Maxwell Chance, of Grosvenor Street, who looks after me, would be more than delighted if you would see me and give him your opinion afterwards' (28 July 1939).

Ten days after the outbreak of World War Two, Shaw wrote from Frinton-on-Sea to Barker in the Channel Islands: 'I am at my wits end for a cure for Charlotte', his wife, who was 'flat on her very painful back', having suffered from being 'yanked out of her bed' during an air raid alarm. He asked when Barker would be within reach again. Guernsey, in Shaw's view, was not 'safe enough for so invaluable a man' (13 September 1939).

*

Unlike their predecessors of exactly a quarter of a century before, not a few of the younger men in Harley Street donned uniform in 1939 with feelings of release. Consultancy work no longer guaranteed a secure and comfortable livelihood. That side of the profession was overcrowded. Rising expenses meant putting up fees, which kept patients away. The sense of vocation wilted under a deadweight of endowment policy premiums incurred in lieu of pensions, and hard to sustain when rents, rates, taxes, and keeping up a certain style, including a preferably enviable make of car, were engulfing incomes and distending overdrafts. The old professional axiom that ten per cent of gross income should be saved was as comically *démodé* as white spats.

Pessimists had been saying that, anyhow, Harley Street was finally in decline, and reduced their estimates of its future from twenty years to ten. The overcrowding, to some degree accentuated by an influx of men with specialist qualifications fleeing from the wrath to come on the Continent, provided cover for strange new standards of practice. An Australian 'gynae' was insisting on a grossly intimate examination of husbands as a preliminary to fitting their wives with a certain contraceptive device. A refugee psychiatrist was pressing his card, boldly inscribed with his newly acquired Harley Street address, on every fresh acquaintance made at social functions. There were less obtrusive forms of exploitation. A general practitioner in a West Country town was paying £100 a year for the right to put at the head of his notepaper a Harley Street address that he never visited. Offered an alternative facility in New Cavendish Street, he indignantly protested that the Harley Street accommodation address was worth 'at least five hundred a year extra' to his provincial practice.

'The unjust competition of these gentlemen' was deplored by a writer in *The Lancet*, who surmised that 'if this war lasts long enough, the Harley Street bogy will be chased out of existence. For shall we all, on our release, return there? Very few.'

The death of Sigmund Freud that autumn, after his year's sanctuary in England, evoked from 49 Harley Street the charge that his 'unhealthy obsession with sex' accounted for 'the depravity of mind and perversity of taste that has affected, among others, English people and particularly English women since the last war'. A reply from 13 Harley Street, also printed in *The Lancet*, suggested that not much permanent harm had been done by Freudian analysts, though parts of their doctrine might be dubious. The writer of the reply did not 'see how Freud can be held responsible for the present prevalence in England of certain *minor* Oriental evils', such as dyed finger-and-toenails, artificial eyebrows, 'and the abundant use of lipstick and face-painting'.

The original correspondent was saluted in verse by Dr Alan McGlashan:

> Hail to thee, blithe spirit!
> In this time of grief
> Thy transcendent merit
> Is to bring relief

To our sad hearts by one big laugh, however brief.

* * *

What thou are one knows not;
What is like thee, pray?
Such a Theory rose not
In mere mortal clay:
To urge thy Muse yet higher! Blame the I.R.A.

In the House of Commons, Sir Ernest Graham-Little, the Wimpole Street, MP, asked the Minister of Health whether he knew that the medical staffs of voluntary hospitals enrolled for full-time war service were being paid salaries that hardly defrayed rent, rates, and taxes, and that 'many distinguished members of the profession were exposed to acute financial distress'. The official reply was that recruitment to the Emergency Medical Service was voluntary, salaries had been agreed on in advance with the medical profession, doctors were free to go on indefinite leave, and in certain circumstances they could be transferred to part-time service.

*

The Emergency Medical Service had been organised in anticipation of air raid casualties to the number of 'at least 300,000' within hours of the outbreak of war. Instead, the improvised hospitals remained empty, their medical staffs idle and resentful because of it. They found that they were officially regarded as 'temporary civil servants', with no consideration shown for the difficulties of adapting, at short notice, their civilian commitments to the new reduced income levels. A surgeon wrote to the medical press: 'I have just received a surtax demand for next Jan 1, which is larger than my gross official salary for a year. I have no claim to a reduction of this assessment.'

Rowley Bristow complained in a letter to Barker in Guernsey: 'The war is really very tiresome.' He had closed 102

Harley Street and moved down into Surrey. Waiting for the
bombs to fall, J. Johnstone Abraham, a Queen Ann Street surgeon known to the reading public by his pen-name of James
Harpole, reflected that while the terms offered to doctors in the
Emergency Medical Service were altogether inadequate for
anyone with Harley Street overheads, 'are we not much better
off than members of the Stock Exchange, the proprietors of
the big empty hotels and restaurants, the unfortunate people
who run theatres, even the Bloomsbury lodging-house keepers
who formerly catered for our students?'

There was hope, and there was fear, that the Emergency
Medical Service was the beginning of a State medical system,
and the end of private practice, in England. Many of the disputants in 1939 and after would have been surprised to know
that the argument had been heard in Army messes during the
1914–18 war. The medical profession became politically conscious when the British Medical Association opposed the
National Insurance Bill in 1911. The Ministry of Health was
transmuted from visionaries' dream into Whitehall reality in
1919. A year or two after, Sir Bertrand Dawson drew up plans
for a medical service that would link general practitioners,
health centres, and hospitals. The doctors were in favour, the
politicians were divided; and the Dawson Report gathered the
dust of the next eighteen years.

A debate in 1939 at the Royal Society of Medicine in Wimpole Street on The Proper Sphere of State Medicine, disclosed
that behind the scenes there had been ardent departmental
thinking about plans for a comprehensive health service in
Great Britain. The cries of dissent aroused by a prominent
speaker's insistence that the function of the State was to encourage its citizens to make voluntary arrangements for medical care on an insurance basis may have echoed dismally in
Harley Street, close by.

In May 1940, the Minister of Health did not 'think it
opportune' to consider a national health service. The next
year, the British Medical Association, in concert with the
Royal Colleges and kindred bodies, organised the Medical

Left : 'To the snob value of Harley Street few of us are immune' (Sir Harold Gillies). The front door of 115a Harley Street is in Devonshire Street. *Below :* At this meeting of the Council of the British Medical Association doctors were finally advised to enter the National Health Service.

Harley Street today—'mini-cars instead of Rolls-Royces.'

Planning Commission. An interim report followed, and little else. The argument in all its complexity was staged before the public in December 1942 with the presentation of the Beveridge Report. One of its parenthetical clauses contained the suggestion that the scope of private practice would be restricted to a point at which it might not be worth preserving.

*

Civil war frustrated Sir Herbert Barker's hope of settling down in his seventies to a life of ease in the Andalusian mountains, though hopeful assurances were received from the Duke of Alba. World war drove him in 1940 from his retreat in the Channel Islands. Forced to move on again, he sought refuge in the Isle of Man, where he could count on the good offices of a former patient, Earl Granville, the Governor. Within a few weeks of his arrival, he was 'unanimously appointed to the staff of Noble's Isle of Man Hospital and Dispensary as Honorary Manipulative Surgeon'.

In those latter years, with the waning of his vitality, his physical strength appeared to be concentrated in his hands. The editor of the local newspaper 'never saw such muscular development in anyone's hands, and yet they are as soft and pliable as a woman's' (*Isle of Man Times*, 5 October 1940). In return for the honour done him by the hospital, Barker undertook to treat patients free at alternate Sunday sessions. For mental relief, he wrote poetry, the hardly inspired, if resolute, self-expression of one seeking consolation in evil times.

TO A FALLEN AIRMAN[1]

Silence and solitude! Now Eventide,
    With mystic touch, is merging Night and Day,
One star—new born—soft lights the azure wide,
    All Nature seems to halt, to pause—and pray!

My eyes grow misty for on such a night
    You left—for ever—your beloved land,

[1] Published in *The Times*, 31 October 1941.

Your engines droning in the dimming light—
Saluting at your officer's command—

I watched you vanish through the opal haze,
I heard your Spitfire's roar wax faint—and cease,
I felt the shadows numbering out your days,
I thought of golden, far-off hours of peace.

And, as I mused, awed by the spell-hushed scene,
A wondering stillness filled the listening air,
More strangely moved than I have ever been
I gazed around—and knew that God was there!

His sojourn in the Isle of Man was made additionally memorable by an incident that for him was an event. It occurred at a gathering of doctors who were to be addressed by a famous visiting member of the faculty, Lord Horder, from London. When the inaugural formalities were over and the Deemsters and others were leaving the hall, Horder observed the retreating figure of Barker among them. He at once sent a message down from the platform enjoining Barker to stay on for the ensuing meeting. 'Sir Herbert Barker's work for suffering humanity,' Horder announced, 'entitles him to be numbered among the greatest of our profession.' The gesture 'met with the cordial approval' of all present (*Isle of Man Times*).

'Glasgow City Engineer Able to Walk Again' a Scottish newspaper proclaimed in headline type. Robert Bruce, Master of Works and City Engineer of Glasgow, had suffered for ten years from fallen arches. He had 'consulted doctors all over the country. Life was becoming a misery. I could scarcely get about,' he told the reporter. He followed Barker to the Isle of Man, besought his help, and was 'put right after some half-dozen manipulations'.

Sir Bruce Bruce-Porter, sequestered by the war at Liss, Hampshire, and 'bored with this spot', wrote to Barker: 'It must be a great joy to you after all to be able to look back on a useful life and the knowledge that you won out in the end.'

He himself had 'some satisfaction' in recalling that Arbuthnot Lane and he had 'fought the orthodox profession for the right of the doctor to teach the public how to avoid illness' (3 February 1944).

Dr R. MacNair Wilson, who had resigned his post as medical correspondent of *The Times* after thirty years, congratulated Barker on his ability to continue working. 'Time goes on proving how great has been your contribution to healing.' One of Wilson's two sons at Eton 'had thought of being a doctor', but he had urged the boy 'to renounce the idea in view of the White Paper which aims at turning us all into servants of the Borough Council'. Wilson was glad that because of his years he would 'never have to work the system' (19 March 1944).

Barker heard himself referred to in public yet again as 'that great friend of suffering humanity' when the Home Secretary, Herbert Morrison, visited the Isle of Man that summer. Morrison was a patient of Barker's. 'How very grateful I am for all your kindness and expert attention', he wrote from Whitehall (6 June 1944). An article on Barker's life work, written for *Picture Post* by the distinguished Liberal journalist, A. J. Cummings, 'brought letters from sufferers in many part of the country', begging to be put in touch with Barker (3 November 1944).

*

During the war years, Lionel Logue frequently set out from 146 Harley Street on what were virtually secret missions to Buckingham Palace and Windsor Castle. The King still counted on Logue's help before most of his speechmaking engagements, and invariably before broadcasting. He never finally mastered his dislike of the microphone, and more than once said that he hated it. For rehearsals of the broadcast to the nation and Commonwealth on Empire Day, 1940, Logue was in attendance for a week in advance, his coaching complicated by the swift movements of history in that crucial month, involving the likelihood of last-minute cuts and interpolations that might increase the King's tensions as a speaker.

Two days after the bombing of Buckingham Palace, Logue wrote to His Majesty: 'It has been my great privilege to be allowed to write you many letters. Never have I written one with such feeling of thankfulness and gratitude to the Most High for your escape from the dastardly attempt on your life ... My own work is at a standstill, as patients cannot travel to see me on account of the constant air raids, and I cannot blame them. Three nights a week I am on all-night duty as an air raid warden' (14 September 1940).

In a broadcast of 23 September 1940, the King announced the creation of the George Cross, 'which will rank next to the Victoria Cross, with the George Medal for wider distribution'. Logue's notes read: 'At 5.40 we went down to the dugout for another run-through, very good. As we were waiting the last few mintues, he suddenly began to laugh and said: "I must write a book called Places I Have Broadcast From". One minute to six, and he is in his armchair, just waiting—always the hardest part of the whole thing. Six o'clock, 3 red lights, and he steps up to the microphone, gives a little smile, and begins. After the first paragraph the All Clear can just be heard —a most dramatic moment. Despite the unpleasant conditions, he spoke splendidly—in a dugout, with an air raid warning on, after having been bombed the week before—a stout effort. He was very tired and pleased when he left for Windsor with the Queen at 6.30.'

In 1941, Logue was noting that ' "c" and "g" still worry him,' and that 'crisis' was one of the more difficult words. He continued to emphasise to all his patients, the King among them, that diaphragm breathing exercises were a valuable factor in toning up the abdominal muscles. He also stressed the importance of making ample use of the expiratory reflexes in ridding the lungs of stale air retained too long, particularly in times of fatigue.

The Keeper of the Privy Purse, Sir Ulick Alexander, was commanded by the King to send Logue a handsome cheque, 'a personal present from His Majesty', who hoped that it would be useful 'in these difficult times'. The thoughtfulness deeply touched Logue, who was 'overwhelmed that the King, with all his responsibilities, should think of me'. His practice, as perhaps the King had realised, was vulnerable in that, apart from the disruption of much of the life of London, many of his patients were of the generation most immediately involved in the war.

On 1 June 1944, he wrote in his notes: 'At 9.30 p.m. the telephone rang, Lascelles speaking from Windsor. "My master wishes to know if you can come to W. tomorrow, Friday, for lunch". Of course I said I would. At W. an air of great tension. The King was in his study with the sunblinds down, still the room was hot. He looked tired and weary. Went through the speech, timed at 5½ minutes. The date of D Day is not exactly fixed, it all depends on the weather.' Logue was to rehearse with the King the call to prayer and dedication that His Majesty would broadcast as soon as the Normandy landings were announced to the world.

Two evenings later, Logue was at Buckingham Palace. 'Just as we were about to begin some voice exercises, a procession of 5 people, including a woman and a policeman, passed along the garden path outside. It stopped all exercises for the time being, as the King was most intrigued by what was happening.' They were watching an attempt to capture a swarm of bees. 'The King got excited, and wanted to go out and give them a hand. It only wanted me to say yes, and he would have opened the window and gone out on to the lawn. It wouldn't do to chance the King being stung by a bee just before a broadcast, so, curious as I was, I had to pretend that I was not interested.'

They went to the improvised broadcasting studio below stairs to rehearse the speech. 'After we returned, the King at once went to the window to see what had happened to the bees, but the people had departed and all that was left was a box under a tree. As I was altering the speech in two places, the door opened and the Queen came in. She gave me her lovely smile, and the King explained, like a schoolboy, what had happened about the bees.' The King's ready surrender to that small distraction can be seen as a symptom of the anxiety that he shared to the full with the war commanders in those critical hours.

Early in January 1945, the King wrote to Logue: 'I wonder if you realise how grateful I am to you for having made it possible for me to carry out this vital part of my job', by which he meant broadcasting. 'I cannot thank you enough.' Logue replied that the King's 'gracious and very welcome letter' gave him more pleasure than he could hope to express. 'We did not dream, when we first began, years ago', he reminded the King, 'that a yearly broadcast would be added to your manifold duties.' New patients often asked him: Will I be able to speak like the King? 'My reply is: "Yes, if you will work like he does".' Logue's letter continued: 'I will cure anyone of intelligence if they will only work as you did, for you are now reaping the benefit of the tremendously hard work you did at the beginning. . . . The greatest pleasure of my life has been the honour of working with you.'

On 5 May 1945, 'the phone rang at 11.30. Sir Alan Lascelles asked me if I would go to Windsor in the afternoon. At 3 a car came from the Palace, and I was in Windsor at 4. Read over the speech with the King and liked it very much. Found him looking weary, and my heart ached for him. We altered some things.' On VE Day, 8 May, there came word that 'the King would like to see you at dinner tonight and bring Mrs Logue', to which 'someone had added the cryptic message, "Tell her to wear something bright".'

Before dinner at the Palace, Logue visited 'the new broadcasting room, which is on the ground floor facing the lawn', and he wrote afterwards that he had been 'through the speech with the King, making one or two small alterations, more for timing than anything else'. As they left, 'the King said plaintively to me: "If I don't get dinner before nine o'clock I won't get any after, as everyone will be away, watching the sights". This sent me into a peal of laughter, and after thinking it over he laughed too, and said: "It *is* funny—but it's quite true".'

After dinner, the King and Logue returned to the broadcasting room, comparing watches with a BBC official. 'We have another run-through. This leaves us just two minutes. One small alteration, and then the Queen, in white, comes in as she always does, to wish him luck. She turns at the door and says, "In your *growly* voice". I take my chair and follow the Queen into the technical room, where Wood of the BBC and his men are altering lights and turning knobs. The Queen in her white dress stands at one window, and I at another, and we both stand rigid for the first two sentences, but the King's voice is gathering strength and power, and we glance at one another and smile, and so we stand until the end. I know the Queen was praying. I was too.'

At the finish of the broadcast, 'I shake the King by both hands and say my heartiest congratulations, and then his wife quietly kisses him and says, "Well done, Bertie!" As I walk back to the Equerries' Room, in my mind I hear two other great broadcasts, the Coronation and the Declaration of War. My good friends crowd round me with congratulations and we all go out into the courtyard again to see the King and Queen come out on to the Balcony. The floodlights are going on at 10.33, and so we talk and wait in this happy, wonderful atmosphere. The flood-lighting goes on, there is a mighty roar from the crowd, and in an instant the scene has become fairyland, with the Royal Standard, lit from beneath, floating in the air.'

Rehearsing the King's speech for the opening of Parliament in November 1945, Logue commented in his notes: 'They seem to try to get tongue-twisters, in such as "in an unbreakable alliance", and "fortified by constant collaboration of the Governments concerned". We could not stand "on windy beaches" for the Home Guard speech, so we made it "storm swept beaches".'

A week later: 'The Home Guard speech was quite good. I went to Windsor for the broadcast. Only one mistake, W in weapons. After the broadcast. I shook hands with the King and congratulated him, and asked why he had stopped on the W. He replied, with a grin: "I did it on purpose". "On purpose?" I ejaculated, and he said: "Yes, if I don't make a mistake, people might not know it was *me*". When I said goodbye, he said to me: "Don't forget the Christmas broadcast".'

Logue was at Windsor again for that annual commitment. The Christmas broadcasts, he noted, 'all have to be cut to pattern, but I think we altered this one less than any other. The King went through it splendidly. We were in his study, with a cheerful fire burning, when he suddenly said: "Logue, I think the time has come when I can do a broadcast by myself, and you can have a Christmas dinner with your family".' Logue wrote: 'I have been expecting this, because he was so confident in the Home Guard broadcast. We discussed the matter thoroughly, and the Queen came in and we looked at it from every angle, and at last decided that the King would be alone in the broadcast.' Saying goodbye, Logue remarked to the Queen: 'You know, Ma'am, I feel like a father who is sending his boy to his first public school'. The Queen 'put her hand on my arm and patted it, and said: "I know just how you feel".'

Listening at home to the Christmas broadcast, Logue was 'astonished when the King's voice came through how firm and resonant it was, and what a lovely tone, and I realised that we had builded better than we knew. All the 3-word breaks had disappeared, and he was speaking confidently and with good inflection and emphasis. Only one stop, at the word God.' As soon as the broadcast had ended, Logue was on the telephone to Windsor Castle. 'In a few seconds his voice came through. A wonderful talk, and when I said: "My job is over, Sir," he said, "Not at all. It is the preliminary work that counts, and that is where you are indispensable." He thanked me and two days later wrote me a very beautiful letter which I hope will be treasured by my dependents.'

That there was therapeutic value for the King in the relaxed relationship established between him and Logue cannot be doubted. The informality that was the keynote is shown in Logue's letters to the King, which he copied into his notes. 'I have worried over you ever since I saw you on the morning of the Guildhall speech. You appeared to me to be absolutely exhausted.' He asked the King's acceptance of some books for his birthday. 'You will enjoy *Empire Builders*. It is very well written and you will realise from it that if it had not been for stupidity on the part of some early settlers, Canada would have extended from Vancouver to Mexico on the Pacific side of the Rocky Mountains.' With a forthcoming broadcast in mind, Logue hoped in writing that the King would not find it fatiguing. 'My thoughts will be with you.'

In another letter, he complimented the King on his speech at the unveiling of the statue to President Roosevelt in Grosvenor Square, London, in April 1948. 'I was particularly interested in the way your voice reacted to the open air. It came through very resonant and powerful. I know you like speaking out of doors—and I must say your voice is better through the microphone.' He told the King, in the same letter, that he had given up working on Wednesdays. 'The strain of my son Tony's 10 months in hospital and my 68 years forces me to take life easier.' He was looking forward to Their Majesties' silver wedding commemoration at St Paul's Cathedral on 26 April 1948. 'You were married just twelve months before we arrived in England.'

Preparing his Christmas broadcast for 1949, the King told Logue that he found it 'difficult to say anything new'. All that he could think of that year, he wrote, was to encourage his people 'to do better' in the year to come. Increasingly, he told Logue, working on the broadcast, worrying about what to say rather than how to say it, tended to spoil Christmas for him. He signed himself, as always, 'Yours very sincerely, GEORGE R.'

To Logue's gift of more books for his birthday in December 1950, the King, in thanking him, deplored the fact that he had so little time to read for pleasure. 'Always those everlasting and unending State papers'. He referred to his having been worried before making a recent speech, while agreeing that 'there are now fewer people who look for my speech defect'. He mentioned again that the Christmas broadcast 'gets more difficult'.

The sharp decline in the King's health in 1951, culminating in the serious lung operation in September that year, brought to an end the long and devoted service of Lionel Logue as mentor and guide to one for whom, as his private and hitherto unpublished notes show, his respect and admiration were unbounded. He followed the course of the King's illness and convalescence with intimate concern. Replying on 16 December to Logue's birthday greetings, His Majesty told him in what was to be a last letter, written from Buckingham Palace: 'I have had a wretched year, from which I seem to be making a remarkable recovery. The latter fact is in many ways entirely due to you.' Before the operation, the surgeon in charge, Price Thomas, had asked to see him breathe. 'When he saw the diaphragm moving up and down naturally, he asked me whether I had always breathed in that way.' To that question the King had replied: 'No, I was taught to breathe in that way in 1926 and I have gone on doing so,' and he told Logue in the letter: 'Another feather in your cap, you see!' As a result, the King added, 'all the exercises I have done since the operation have come very easily to me, due to right breathing, I find'. He died in his sleep at Sandringham seven weeks later, on 5 February 1952.

As a mark of his personal favour, the King had made Logue a Commander of the Royal Victorian Order. To one of his closest friends, Logue confided his hope of receiving a knighthood. That it was not fulfilled never became a grievance. He was happy in the assurance that he had gained the esteem of one to whom he referred to in his notes as 'the greatest man in the world'.

XII

LORD HORDER, RESISTANCE LEADER

Bombs probably intended for Euston railway terminus brought chaos to Harley Street. Several of its houses were demolished, leaving gaps more unsightly than those that were a legacy of the South Sea Bubble two hundred and twenty years earlier. The remaining medical population, mostly superannuated, unfit for Service life, or holders of hospital posts in and near London, was considerably outnumbered by the brass and chromium name-plates gleaming amid the dust of desolation. Notices of removal to other addresses appeared on many doors.

The Doctor's Dilemma, put on at the Haymarket Theatre, London, in 1942, for what was to be the longest run of any Shaw revival up to that time, was like a funeral oration read over the ruthlessly exposed foundations of Nos 30, 32, 34, 36, and other blitzed Harley Street houses. 'Ours is not a profession but a conspiracy,' a line in the play that startled Edwardian first-nighters, fell on the ears of a more responsive generation of theatre-goers. Newcomers to the play were surprised to find that it contained only one reference to socialised medicine. The laughter that greeted the appearances of those professional stereotypes, Sir Colenso Ridgeon and Sir Bloomfield Bonington, with their talk of 'stimulating the phagocytes', and their confused notions of vaccines and anti-toxins, showed that Shaw's derision of aspects of private practice was in tune with a quickening public sentiment.

Harley Street men returning from the armed forces were suspiciously regarded by those who had maintained their civilian status. It was feared that Service experience might have conditioned them to uncritical acceptance of the propaganda for a State medical system. In 1945, no ex-Service medical man was elected to any of the committees of the Marylebone Division of the British Medical Association. The largest division in the Association, it represented Harley Street and its conjoint areas, where tensions flashed like black lightning as the atmosphere became charged with the devious politics of the National Health Service. The Labour Party victory in 1945 was an electoral shock to which the doctors were as acutely sensitive as the deposed political party. Medicine as a public facility, which is how the protagonists of the Health Service saw it, meant to their no less sincere opponents medicine degraded to a public utility.

In the autumn of that year, Sir Herbert Barker wrote to Shaw soliciting a donation to a fund for the endowment of a Barker Bed at St Thomas's Hospital. Shaw replied that Barker ought not to 'tout for the Hospital' on behalf of a memorial to himself. In any event, he never subscribed to hospitals, 'which should all be maintained by the State'. Shaw's still distinctive handwriting was at last faltering before the onset of time. He was finding it 'impossible to indulge in the luxury of friendly correspondence', and asked Barker to believe that he was 'years in arrear with professional work, business, and arrangements for my death'. If it was decided to put up a Barker statue on the Embankment, then he would gladly give his mite (12 September 1945).

'The doctors are too narrowly educated', was the criticism made of them to the present writer by the Minister of Health, Aneurin Bevan, esconced with authoritative amplitude at his Whitehall desk. Nor did he conceal his disrespect for their spokesmen, whose contribution to the National Health Service negotiations was disfigured by muddled thinking and divided counsels. What to some was unseemly ministerial impatience may, after all, have been to the profession's advantage. More protracted political reflection might have finally extinguished the doctors' liberty of action. A sufficient margin remained in which one of the first notable postwar protest movements, the

Fellowship for Freedom in Medicine, could manoeuvre and flourish. Its object was summarised in Clause 2 of its six-point programme: 'To protect the public and the medical profession from State monopoly in medicine.' The Fellowship's founder and chief animating spirit was Baron Horder of Ashford in the County of Southampton, GCVO, MD, BSC, (Lond.), DCL, FRCP, familiarly known up and down Harley Street as 'Tommy' Horder.

*

His was still a household name, that of the doctor of whom it was once said that no eminent patient was allowed to die before he had been called in to give his assent. But he was no longer the much sought-after consultant who signed bulletins about the health of princes and prime ministers. Blanks had begun to appear in his appointment book a little before the Second World War. He was nearing his seventies, and younger and scientifically better equipped men were overtaking him in the diagnostic percipience on which his Harley Street reputation rested. Not a few of those up-and-coming rivals had profited by the clinical teaching to which he gave long and devoted service at his old hospital, St Bartholomew's.

After thirty years of highly successful practice, he was beset by moods of frustration that ill-accorded with his vocational dominance and his normally agreeable and often attractive temperament. Those discordant lapses had two focal points: his failure in nine successive annual ballots for the presidency of the Royal College of Physicians, and Churchill's preference for Sir Charles McMoran Wilson (subsequently Lord Moran), as his personal physician during the Second World War and after. Both were deep disappointments that left their mark. As to the second, Horder's vehemence touched bitterness, with Lord Beaverbrook, who had been one of the first of his Harley Street patients, cited as the malign influence that had worked against him.[1]

A statistic of the 1930s was that more than two out of five

[1] Lord Horder spoke forcibly to me on the subject on two occasions.-R.P.

doctors on the Medical Register came from Scotland. Casually, it might have been conjectured that the West Country supplied the remainder. Horder was born at Shaftesbury in 1871, the son of a draper whose business, established in High Street, Swindon, is still conducted by a member of the family. He took his MB with first-class honours, carried off various gold medals, and arrived in Harley Street at the age of thirty-one. He was soon the owner of a Rolls-Royce, which he kept discreetly out of sight in a side street when he visited Barts. He claimed to be the first consulting physician without a private income to be appointed to the honorary staff of that hospital.

At the beginning, he made his earnings up to a thousand a year by coaching medical students at evening classes held at 141 Harley Street, taken on a long lease. The connection yielded later dividends when the students, having qualified, sent him patients from all over the country. It was the foundation of a practice that became one of the more solid buttresses of Harley Street prestige between the wars.

In those years, the peak of his career, few days passed on which he did not see twenty patients in his consulting-room, and no week, it seemed, in which he was not at the bedside of some distinguished, famous, or merely wealthy, invalid. One of his juniors, still in Harley Street, holds fast to his opinion that 'Tommy was a bit of a snob', and recalls Horder's anger at being rung up late one night about a case. When his colleague explained that the patient concerned was a niece of Lord Cushendun (formerly Ronald McNeill, MP), 'his tone changed at once—he was all ears, and promised to see the patient early next morning'. Another stubbornly surviving recollection is of his upsetting the Medical Society of London by arriving an hour late to deliver his presidential address. 'He had been seeing Lord Somebody at Claridge's.' There were sardonic references to his *Who's Who* entry, '*educ*: privately', depriving Swindon High School of the credit for its part in tutoring one of the most accomplished medical intelligences of our time.

To set against that social bias, there was his distinguished behaviour as a great hospital teacher. He might be lunching with royalty, a cabinet minister, or congenial friends at a club: no matter how imposing or beguiling the company, he would not be deflected from his early afternoon teaching session in the wards at Barts. It could be more engrossing than private practice. Once, towards the end of a long round of the wards, lasting nearly two hours, he was given a telephone message by a loud-voiced porter at the hospital. 'The Mayor of Banbury presents 'is compliments and wants to know whether 'e should wait any longer stark naked be'ind that screen of yours in 'arley Street.'

An old colleague of Horder's, now retired, says that 'he was mean about money', and recalls the father who took his son to see Horder on the advice of their family doctor. Charging ten guineas for the consultation, Horder waved aside the father's offer of a cheque, and demanded cash. Father and son turned out their pockets to produce the amount. They were left with a couple of shillings between them. 'It didn't bother Horder that they might have to pay their fares home'.

He developed other money foibles, including an unconvincing pretence that he feared poverty. While it never became anything like a clinically familiar delusion, he lapsed into a curiously furtive phase in his closing years. Having left 141 Harley Street, he saw patients in a rather shabby green-decorated consulting-room in Devonshire Place. He then transferred his practice to Nottingham Place, where he rented a room from the Cremation Society. For consultations with his remaining few patients of lofty estate, he borrowed the rooms of friends in Harley Street.

The Fellowship for Freedom in Medicine, which pre-occupied him at a time when private practice languished, had for its charter the letter from him published in the *British Medical Journal* a month before the National Health Service Act came into operation in July 1948. Expressing the doubts of many in the profession, the letter resulted in an inaugural meeting at Caxton Hall, Westminster, the following November. Medical men converged there from many parts of the

country, and Horder, by then seventy-eight, became a resistance leader with 1,700 determined doctors formed up behind
him.

At the Caxton Hall meeting he spoke of 'the dragooning of
the profession by politicians', and of 'the machinations of mischievous and meddlesome men, holding key positions' outside
the British Medical Association. 'From the very start, we have
lacked dignity and a due appreciation of our use and value in
society. We let ourselves be used as pawns in the game instead
of master pieces. Our own weakness was partly responsible for
the fact that the National Service Act was born in dishonour.'
Resigning various honorary appointments, of which he had
borne his full share through many years, he declaimed from
many platforms his creed, 'Put not your faith in politicians,
they come and go, but medicine goes on for ever,' and set
about building the Fellowship into a rampart against what for
him were the forces of national folly.

To that cause he gave his last resources of zest. He was like
a gnomic figure guarding not arcane secrets but the values of his
class and kind. Trim, precise, quick-witted, and courageous,
he was one of those small-stature men whose robust and
wilful personalities cast a larger-than-life shadow. He was no
seeker after power. His belief in the doctor's mission, and
especially in the family doctor's role, on which the honour of
the profession so largely rested, was movingly sincere, his fear
that the politicians would compromise it deep-seated.

Events have warranted his foresight, if not his chief anxie-
ties. Above all, they have confirmed the dispiriting epitaph
that Harley Street will not see the like of him again.

*

Sir Herbert Barker's name was on the dwindling list of Lord
Horder's patients. 'I am sorry that you need my advice',
Horder wrote to him from Devonshire Place. 'Of course I will
give it to you,' appending the hardly enheartening informa-
tions: 'Poor Rivett Carnac was under my care, but I couldn't
save him' (9 October 1947).

Approaching octogenarianism, Barker was not what Horder would have called 'a well man'. He had gone back to Jersey in 1946, hoping to enjoy a larger measure of retirement than so far had been vouchsafed to him. His telephone rang as imperiously as before. Telegraph messengers were daily at his door, appealing letters arrived by every mail, some of them from doctors, wishing to send him their patients. His wrists were still remarkably efficient, his fingers still sensitive. 'You are an angel of light', the Duchess of Hamilton told him in a letter of gratitude for services to her son, Lord Malcolm Douglas-Hamilton, severely hurt 'in an 80 ft. fall'.

Ironically, the hands that to so many seemed to be endowed with magical powers were disabled when Barker himself had a fall in 1947. Ruefully surveying them, he remarked: 'I still hope to go on until I'm a hundred—in fact, my goal is a hundred and five.' On 22 July 1950, three successive home news bulletins of the BBC told the listening public: 'The death was announced last night of Sir Herbert Barker, the manipulative surgeon. He was eighty-one'. *The Times* obituary notice said that by challenging professional skill he had increased it.

Augustus John, who had been 'moving about France', wrote to Lady Barker 'as one of Boneo's innumerable creditors and friends'. He was 'much upset' (underlined) by the news. 'He did not live in vain' (4 August 1950). Whether from excess of feeling or from a memory slip, he wrote to Barker's widow again, explaining that he had been away in France, and had only just heard of her great loss. 'I thought he was indestructible. It was a fine life and multitudes of people, like me, have to thank him daily for his skill and understanding' (15 August 1950).

*

In December 1952, the *British Medical Journal* discussed the recession from Harley Street, 'if such is taking place'. Objections to maintaining the street's medical exclusiveness were raised at an inquiry into London County Council development plans. The *Journal* agreed that while Harley

Street 'has never been exactly attractive to the eye', it had a dignity 'that consorted well' with the consultant side of medical practice. That no 'To Let' boards were to be seen was not necessarily proof of continuing prosperity. The chief ground landlords, Howard De Walden Estates, still have an aesthetic objection to them.

In the '50s, the professional population totalled 673, according to a name-plate check. But some consultants do not display their names; and the census did not include the cluster of specialists with consulting-rooms at 149 Harley Street (London Clinic). Clearly, recession was not taking place in any exodus sense.

What was happening was a breach in the long and jealously sustained professional exclusiveness of the street. At its once highly favoured 'best end', where it joins Cavendish Square, leases were being resold to solicitors, consulting engineers, quantity surveyors, and other non-medical people, including a carpet manufacturer (at No 1). To the older generation of specialists it was not recession but retrogression. In part, it explained why, with the approach of the '60s, the demand for consulting-rooms outran their availability. More particularly, the new pressure on accommodation came from ambitious younger men with nationalised hospital appointments that left them with enough free time to augment their incomes by private practice. The local estate agents know them as part-timers. The applicants' lists were headed by gynaecologists and psychiatrists. After them came American osteopaths looking for an 'office' in Harley Street, psychotherapists, faith healers, nature cure practitioners, dentists.

Dilution was arrested by the Howard De Walden Estates acting in agreement with the Westminster planning authority. Would-be newcomers to Harley Street were rigorously 'vetted' and many rejected out of hand. The policy was not utterly partisan. In formulating it consideration was given to guaranteeing the probity of a national asset that was developing a growth-rate of prestige abroad in excess of that at home, where the pillars were shaken by socialised medicine and the scepticism of a generation dead against orthodoxy. In these later '60s, the percentage of foreign patients seen in the consultants' waiting rooms is probably higher than it ever was before. Americans fly over for Harley Street check-ups and Savile Row measuring sessions in the same trip. Appointments are made by telephone with oil sheiks of the Arabian Gulf and the new plutocrats of East and Central African politics. Harley Street men whose names would not immediately identify them to most people are well-known to British Overseas Airways hostesses, especially those on flights to the Middle East.

*

Recession has occurred not in Harley Street lettings but in the medicine of 'great names' and Olympian second opinions. There have been notable doctors since Dawson and Horder, but not in the old sense of high public esteem. Sir Horace Evans, of Weymouth Street, whose subsequent peerage, as Lord Evans, blurred his identity in the popular mind, had a long and distinguished record of service to the Royal Family. He was not conceded a place in *Who's Who* until after the Second World War, and he did not become a public figure in a headline sense until 1956, the year of the Suez crisis, when he was medical adviser to an overwrought Prime Minister. Horder, who had attended Bonar Law, Ramsay MacDonald, and Neville Chamberlain, once asked rhetorically in a lecture: 'Who knows how much turns on whether a Prime Minister's pipe is clean or foul?' Dawson's advice to Lloyd George in 1940, not to accept the post of British ambassador at Washington, was decisive. That Horace Evans influenced any of the currents of history may be doubted. He succeeded Dawson at Court as physician to Queen Mary and to King George VI and Queen Elizabeth (now the Queen Mother). His personal style was that of a conformist serving the established order with distinguished efficiency.

As a doctor, examining a patient, he used his finger tips with a feline precision suggesting that he received more authentic information through them than through his stethoscope. It was an impressive adjunct of his clinical flair, which was envied by his colleagues. With it there went charm, kindness, and consideration, virtues that adorned both his professional and private life. His fastidious manner did not ratify his taste for conviviality in Bohemian company, or his worldliness in endorsing an oil millionaire's self-prescription of a new young mistress every year for rejuvenation purposes. Those who saw Evans only in the consulting-room might have been no less surprised by his recondite knowledge of racehorse form. His death from throat cancer in 1963 was a great loss to the faculty. It was also a reminder that the age of resounding Harley Street reputations had passed.

Lord Moran did not fit into that context, his being chiefly a vicarious fame, deriving from his rôle as medical squire to Sir Winston Churchill, KG, and augmented by the publication in 1966 of his controversial diaries. He had a Harley Street practice, but his professional repute was largely centred in the life of a great hospital. For twenty-five of his best years he was Dean of the Medical School at St Mary's, Paddington, the prestige of which institution was greatly enhanced during the term of his leadership.

The text for his Harveian Oration at the Royal College of Physicians in 1953 was taken from the report of the Royal Commission on university education of forty years before— 'the most important document of my time'. He quoted the Commission's finding that 'the inhabitants of Harley Street and Wimpole Street had been so taken up with their private practices that they had neglected to add to knowledge. The pursuit of learning had been handicapped by the pursuit of gain.'[1]

*

For many patients, still, including Green Belt stockbrokers who talk airily of 'running up to town to see my quack', an address in Harley Street ranks as a high medical degree. They sustain a panache that was not expected to survive the new dis-

[1] See page 32.

pensation in medicine dating from 1948. The then Minister of Health visualised the new Service as finally comprehensive, and classed as eccentrics those who might continue to seek help in the private sector. 'I don't intend to interfere with private practice. If anyone wishes to buy the services of a doctor, a physiotherapist, a herbalist, or anyone else, I don't propose to stop them.' It was not a concession; it was an intimation of the responsible authority's hope that a shaky if not rotten limb of the tree would soon wither away.

It has not done so. The main trunk has had to be shored up, while the suspect branch flourishes with the growth of private-practice insurance, such as that provided by the efficient and expanding British United Provident Association. A recent survey in *The Times* suggested, as its conclusion, that 'the Government consider the possibility that the salvation of the NHS may lie in the private sector'.[1]

That minicars instead of Rolls-Royces are now more common in and around Harley Street is a symptom of the traffic problem, not of lost pre-eminence. Taximen are still incited to wry comment when fares ask to be driven to 90A or 93A Harley Street, which are in Weymouth Street, or 112A, 114A, 115A and 117A Harley Street, which have their front doors in Devonshire Street. Those addresses, and others, known in the local estate offices as 'dwarf' houses, are conversions from the former coachhouses and stabling of adjacent Harley Street establishments. Their medical occupiers have a legitimate claim to be numbered with the elect round the corner. Even so, it is hard to dispel the impression of a slightly spurious lustre.

The same sense of coveted propinquity pervades the caretaking milieu below stairs in those capacious Harley Street basements that in some instances provide overflow consulting-room accommodation. There is a waiting list of couples ready to step into vacancies that offer £9–10 a week, with no rent, rates, or lighting and heating bills to pay, plus the satisfaction of a Harley Street address. Some of the caretakers' quarters are decorated and furnished with a nicety outpointing that of

[1] *Two Kinds of Health*, by Patrick Wood (June 1966).

the doctors above, where the prevailing environmental tone, up and down the street, is oppressively tasteless.

Although the old opulence, with its baronetcies and butlers, is now hardly a memory, a new race of specialists is renting suites at £1,000 a year and more, instead of single rooms at £300–400, and equipping them with apparatus and facilities that add another dimension to Harley Street practice. As well as advice and prescriptions, the patient now gets X-rays, a variety of tests and minor operations, formerly available only at hospitals and nursing homes, Some of the suites have the semblance of well-found clinics. The scientific method has invaded consulting-rooms where once the frock-coated sages of Harley Street laboured the obvious in homilies on nervous tension, necessary sleep, bowel regulation, and the wisdom of the ancient Greek precept of nothing too much.

The frock coats have long gone; the last habitual wearer of the top hat in Harley Street, W. G. Howarth, FRCS, retired in the '50s; yet it is still a surprise, if not a shock, to be greeted by a specialist in a white coat. The doubt grows that patients are regarded less as human beings and more as laboratory specimens. Physicians have ceased to be philosophers and are becoming technicians. The Renaissance view of the individual, implicitly upheld by the great doctors, may have vanished with the silk lapels and white spats.

*

Encroaching on traditional practice today are new concepts of the healing art that are widening, if not necessarily advancing, the frontiers of medicine. The osteopath is no longer a trespasser in Harley Street. Acupuncture, ancient in lineage but novel as an adjunct of orthodoxy, is being practised there. Hypnosis has been accepted as one of the permissible new therapies. Radiesthesia, which applies 'dowsing' techniques to medical problems, is the preoccupation of several specialists, one of whom identifies with it 'the power which so filled Jesus that the very hem of his garment was alive with it'.[1]

[1] Michael Ash, MRCS, LRCP.

Close by, at 26 Queen Anne Street, The Guild of Health, founded in 1904 by Dr Percy Dearmer and Conrad Noel, exists 'to restore the healing ministry of Christ in and through His Church'. Its patrons' list and membership includes physicians and surgeons, who incorporate the Guild's principles in their practices.[1] 'Official medicine frowns on spiritual healing, but many doctors are privately sympathetic.'[2] Some, like A. Dickson Wright, FRCS, a past president of the Royal College of Surgeons, are sceptical. At a Guild of Health teach-in, 'he was very scornful in his remarks about seeking help from the "spirit people"'.[3]

These and other fringe activities may be less of a threat to the integrity of Harley Street than those of its qualified practitioners who, in concert with psychiatrists, minister to the squalid contemporary traffic in sexual promiscuity and abortion. Stiletto-heel marks honeycombing the linoleum outside some consulting-room doors are the *graffiti* of disgraceful professional exploitation as well as of personal folly. Harley Street respectability cloaks alike the just and the unjust. It glosses those who warrant Voltaire's sneer that physicians 'pour drugs of which they know little into bodies of which they know less,' and those who, as Osler said, 'practise with their brains or with their tongues'.

Such amoral or indifferent attitudes as may exist behind those solid eighteenth-century doors cannot confound the truth that Harley Street today, as yesterday, essentially preserves the best traditions, dispenses the best advice, and maintains the highest standards, of any system of medicine in the world.

[1] See *A Doctor Heals by Faith*: Christopher Woodard (Hodder,1959).
[2] 'For Health and Healing', *The Guild of Health Monthly*, May–June, 1966.
[3] Ibid.

INDEX